BLUEPRINTS

Mental Arithmetic Key Stage 2

Liz Hopkins

Stanley Thornes (Publishers) Ltd

Stanley Thornes for TEACHERS:
BLUEPRINTS • PRIMARY COLOURS • LEARNING TARGETS

Stanley Thornes for Teachers publishes practical teacher's ideas books and photocopiable resources for use in primary schools. Our three key series, **Blueprints**, **Primary Colours** and **Learning Targets** together provide busy teachers with unbeatable curriculum coverage, inspiration and value for money. We mail teachers and schools about our books regularly. To join the mailing list simply photocopy and complete the form below and return using the **FREEPOST** address to receive regular updates on our new and existing titles. You may also like to add the name of a friend who would be interested in being on the mailing list. Books can be bought by credit card over the telephone and information obtained on (01242) 267280.

Please add my name to the *Stanley Thornes for* **TEACHERS** mailing list.

Mr/Mrs/Miss/Ms _____

Address _____

_____ postcode _____

School address _____

_____ postcode _____

Please also send information about *Stanley Thornes for* **TEACHERS** to:

Mr/Mrs/Miss/Ms _____

Address _____

_____ postcode _____

To: Marketing Services Dept., Stanley Thornes Ltd, FREEPOST (GR 782), Cheltenham, GL50 1BR

Text © Liz Hopkins 1998
Original line illustrations © Stanley Thornes (Publishers) Ltd 1998

First published in 1998 by
Stanley Thornes (Publishers) Ltd

Reprinted in 2002 by:
Nelson Thornes Ltd
Delta Place
27 Bath Road
Cheltenham GL53 7TH
United Kingdom

A catalogue record for this book is available from the British Library.

ISBN 0–7487–3584–4

Typeset by Tech-Set Ltd.
Printed and bound in Great Britain by The Bath Press

02 03 04 05 06 / 10 9 8 7 6 5

Contents

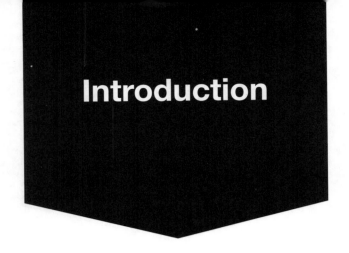

Introduction

Blueprints Mental Arithmetic is a carefully structured book, tied to the National Curriculum, offering an interactive approach to improving children's mental facility in mathematics.

It is divided into three sections. The first section covers the 10 Main Topics of the book with ideas for teaching and copymasters for consolidation. There are two copymasters on each page, divided by a dotted line to indicate that the page can be cut in two to allow the copymasters to be completed at different times. The second section covers Associated Topics for which there are copymasters but no teacher's notes; and the final section comprises tests and quick maths copymasters.

How to use this book ▷

Main Topics

The teacher's notes are divided into National Curriculum Level 3 and National Curriculum Level 4/5 and list the copymasters appropriate at each level. The copymasters are grouped together after the teacher's notes.

The teacher's notes covering the 10 main topics of the book contain a wealth of ideas that can be used with groups or the whole class. The section includes many strategies for learning and each idea and copymaster is clearly linked to the Learning Objectives listed at the start of each topic and in the contents at the start of the section.

The ideas for whole class work are designed to encourage children to take an active part in learning, involving question and answer sessions. It is suggested that these topics are tackled in blocks of one or two weeks, integrating the whole class ideas and the copymasters. Many copymasters are self-explanatory, but some may require additional teacher input.

Associated Topics

There are no teacher's notes for this section as its main purpose is revision, practice and assessment. The section comprises copymasters that are ideally suited for individual or group revision of core work. Some copymasters are aimed at Level 5. The copymasters are linked to the Learning Objectives listed in the contents at the start of the section.

It is suggested that they are used a short time after the children have studied a topic in their core mathematics work, hence consolidating and applying their knowledge and understanding. A short mental revision session could be followed by children completing an appropriate copymaster.

Reinforcement and Assessment

There are no teacher's notes as this section provides practice of the four rules of number and assessment of the work covered in this book. The copymasters are linked to the Learning Objectives listed in the contents at the start of the section.

The topic tests can be used to provide a valuable assessment of the children's grasp of mental arithmetic at regular intervals throughout the year. Most of the tests combine two topics. The tests are aimed at Level 3 and Level 4 and there are extension tests aimed at Level 5. Having completed a test, you may wish to work through sections of it with small groups or return to some of the ideas for whole class work, or repeat copymasters.

For quick number practice there are number grids for addition, subtraction and multiplication, all of which can be done against the clock. The children can then repeat the grid at a later date and try to improve their performance.

The quick maths copymasters can be used in the same way. The sets of questions can be done one at a time over a number of days or one after the other during the same session. Most children really enjoy the challenge of beating their personal best. It may be appropriate to remind the children of some of the strategies they have for number work before they attempt a copymaster.

The mental arithmetic tests provide practice for the Key Stage 2 tests. They provide mixed questions in the style of the National Curriculum Mental Arithmetic Tests. There are copymaster answer sheets for the children and questions for the teacher to read aloud. Tests 3 and 4 are aimed mainly at Level 4; test 5 is aimed at Level 5.

Main Topics

Place Value ▷

Addition ▷

Subtraction ▷

Multiplication ▷

Division ▷

Number Patterns ▷

Fractions ▷

Decimals ▷

Money ▷

Time ▷

Place Value

Learning Objectives

To be able to:
1. Understand that the position of the digit gives its value
2. Add or subtract 1, 10 and 100
3. Understand place value to 1000
4. Round numbers to nearest 100
5. Order numbers

1 THE POSITION OF THE DIGIT GIVES ITS VALUE

Ideas for whole class work

1 This is an excellent activity for reinforcing that a three, for example, can be worth 3, 30, or 300, depending on its position in a multi-digit number.

Write a three-digit number on the board. The idea is to turn each digit in turn into 0 by subtraction. For example, 374: to turn the 7 into 0, subtract 70; to turn the 3 into 0, subtract 300; and finally, subtract 4. Demonstrate this with other numbers. Sometimes, subtract the tens first and sometimes the hundreds first. The children can play with this in pairs using a calculator. The first player enters a number and second player subtracts to 0 in a given order.

2 You need some cards with three-digit numbers on them. Invite three children to the front and give each one a card. Encourage the rest of the class to put the children in order according to the numbers on the cards. Get them to justify the order they choose which will help them to develop their vocabulary and clarify their thinking. Build up to five cards and eventually use more than five. To make it more challenging, use sets of numbers made up of the same digits in different orders, eg 467 and 674, 469 and 649.

Copymasters
None.

2 ADD OR SUBTRACT 1, 10 AND 100

C1

Ideas for whole class work

1 Add or subtract 1. This is best done with calculators. Enabling the children to see the digit change is a valuable exercise. This really brings to life the idea of what comes after the 9 in the units column.

The children work in pairs. Tell them to enter a single-digit number, then press add (+) and 1, and to keep pressing equals (=). Get them to observe closely as the digits change. Emphasize what happens after 9 (it always changes to 0 with the tens digit increasing by 1). This may seem obvious but when children see it happen their understanding is clearer.

2 Add or subtract 10 or 100. You need a calculator between two. Tell the children to enter a small two-digit number, eg 15, then press add (+) and 10 and to keep pressing equals (=). Encourage them to observe which digit changes and which stays the same. Repeat this exercise, starting with different two-digit numbers. Follow this by giving them various two-digit numbers and asking them to add or subtract 10. If they understand place value they can easily add and subtract 10 by changing the right digit.

Next, get the children to enter a three-digit number and ask them to add 100.

Copymasters
C1 Place Value *Add 10 or 1* The copymaster has a variety of three-digit numbers on it. The idea is that the children know in which column the digit increases without actually having to add on.

Read out the following instructions for the children to apply to the numbers on their sheets: (1) add 1; (2) add 10; (3) add 10; (4) add 1; (5) add 1; (6) add 10; (7) add 1; (8) add 10; (9) add 10; (10) add 1. This copymaster can be used again with other instructions.

3 UNDERSTAND PLACE VALUE TO 1000

This is covered by the other Learning Objectives in this topic, particularly by Learning Objective 1: Understand that the position of the digit gives its value.

4 ROUND NUMBERS TO NEAREST 100

C2

Ideas for whole class work

1 Draw a number line and label it 0, 100, 200, 300. Plot a point near to 200. Get the children to suggest possible values for it. Plot other points, gradually moving closer to the half-way point and discuss with them what happens at 150. Following this, plot points near to 100 and 300. Reverse the process and get the children to plot given numbers on the line. Next, change it round and plot a number and ask the children to tell you the nearest hundred.

Copymasters
C2 Place Value *Round to the nearest 100*

5 ORDER NUMBERS

C3-4

Ideas for whole class work

Choose three digits at random. Get the children to arrange these to make different three-digit numbers. Encourage them to be organized so that they know when they have all the possible arrangements (there are six). Suggest they start with the smallest possible number that can be made from the digits and work up to the largest one. When they have done this, select another set of digits and get the children to list all the possible combinations starting with the largest number. Encourage the children to look at and discuss the values of the digits.

Copymasters

C3 Place Value *Order numbers* The children should write a given number in the correct box. Any three-digit numbers can be used but you could start with the following: 220, 570, 701, 99, 352, 750, 652, 194, 101, 290, 301, 799, 600, 402. The copymaster can be used again with other sets of numbers.

C4 Place Value *Order numbers* On this copymaster, the children should put the correct sign in each box: = (equals), > (greater than), < (less than).

LEVEL **4/5**

Learning Objectives

To be able to:
1. Multiply and divide by 10, 100, and 1000

2. Understand that the position of the digit gives its value
3. Round off

1 MULTIPLY AND DIVIDE BY 10, 100 AND 1000

C5-8

Ideas for whole class work

1 The children's understanding that digits change their value when they change columns is helped by multiplying and dividing by 10 or 100. Start with a single-digit number and keep multiplying by 10. Ask individual children to tell you what the next number is when they multiply by 10. For example, start with 4 and encourage them to tell you 40, 400, 4000, and so on.

This exercise can also be used for dividing by 10; for example, start with 500000 and ask individual children to tell you what the next number is when they divide by 10, ie 50000, 5000, and so on.

Some children will be able to grasp this principal when working with decimals, eg 0·003, 0·03, 0·3, and they should be encouraged to do the multiplications and divisions using simple decimals (you may wish to insert the noughts in the decimals to comply with the convention).

2 This is like 'I went to the shops and I bought . . .' Choose a single-digit number, multiply it by 10 and add some units. Repeat this several times. For example, $4 \times 10 + 3 = 43$; $43 \times 10 + 6 = 436$; $436 \times 10 + 1 = 4361$; and so on. This is very good for the children's concentration and their visualization of the columns:

```
    4
   43
  436
 4361
```

To start with, write the numbers on the board so that they can see the diagonal pattern. Then try doing it without writing down the numbers.

Copymasters

C5 Place Value *Multiply/divide by 10/100/1000* The copymaster has two sets of numbers. Tell the children what to multiply or divide each number by.

  (1) divide by 10
  (2) multiply by 10
  (3) divide by 10
  (4) multiply by 10
  (5) divide by 100
  (6) multiply by 100
  (7) divide by 100
  (8) multiply by 1000
  (9) divide by 1000
(10) multiply by 100

The answers are all whole numbers in set A. Set B uses decimals. The same operations can be used with both sets. This copymaster can be used again with other operations.

C6 Place Value *Multiply by 10*

C7 Place Value *Divide/multiply: 10/100*

C8 Place Value *Divide/multiply: 10/100*

2 THE POSITION OF THE DIGIT GIVES ITS VALUE

C1
C9-10

Ideas for whole class work

1 Choose a digit and a column value and ask the children to tell you numbers that fit these criteria, eg digit, seven; column value, hundreds. The children can give you numbers such as 702, 1765 and 12 780. Encourage them to wrap the digit in a larger number. Give challenges to individual children, such as asking them to give you a five-digit number with a three worth tens.

2 Write a four-digit number on the board. The idea is to turn each digit into 0 by subtraction, step by step. For example, 4398: to get rid of the 3, subtract 300; to get rid of the 4, subtract 4 000, and so on. Do this with other four-digit numbers, varying the order of attack. The children can then do this in pairs with a calculator. One enters a number and challenges their partner to get rid of a certain digit by a single subtraction. The partner then hands the calculator back to the challenger and challenges them to remove another digit by subtraction, and so on.

Copymasters

C1 Place Value *Add 10 or 1*

C9 Place Value *Position gives value* The copymaster has three-, four- and five-digit numbers on it. Tell the children which digit to make into 0. The children need to identify the value of the given digit in order to make it into 0 by subtraction.

(1) subtract to make the 3 into 0
(2) subtract to make the 5 into 0
(3) subtract to make the 9 into 0
(4) subtract to make the 8 into 0
(5) subtract to make the 3 into 0
(6) subtract to make the 4 into 0
(7) subtract to make the 7 into 0
(8) subtract to make the 2 into 0
(9) subtract to make the 4 into 0
(10) subtract to make the 6 into 0

This copymaster can be used again making different digits into nought.

C10 Place Value *Position gives value*

3 ROUNDING OFF

Ideas for whole class work

Write some three-digit numbers on the board, some of which round off to 200. Through discussion, encourage the children to identify the ones which round off to 200. Get the children to suggest numbers which round off to, for example, 500. Focus on the fact that some of the numbers given are more than 500 and some of them are less than 500. Identify the largest and smallest numbers which would round off to 500. Do this with other hundreds. This idea can be extended to thousands.

Copymasters

None.

Addition

LEVEL 3

Learning Objectives

To be able to:
1. Recall mentally up to 20
2. Add up to 100
3. Add up to multiples of 10
4. Round and approximate

1 RECALL MENTALLY UP TO 20

C11

Ideas for whole class work

1 It is essential that the children learn bonds to 20 in the same way as bonds to 10. From this they can then generalize for addition up to 100 and beyond.

List all the possible pairs that make 10. Show how these can be used to make pairs of numbers that make 20 by adding 10 to one or other of the numbers, eg 8 + 2 = 10 gives 18 + 2 and 8 + 12. Get the children to practise this. If you give them a pair of numbers that make 10, they have to respond with a pair of numbers that make 20.

2 This is a quick, simple activity. Give the children a number less than 20 and ask them for the number which makes it up to 20. Getting the children to put up their thumbs, rather than their hands, when they are ready puts less pressure on those who need a little longer to work out the answer.

Copymasters

C11 Addition *Bonds of 20* The copymaster can be used several times against the clock to try to improve personal performance.

2 ADD UP TO 100
C12

Ideas for whole class work
Get the children to tell you pairs of multiples of 10 that add up to 100, eg 30 + 70, 10 + 90. List them in order on the board and note the pattern (as one number increases by 10, the other decreases correspondingly). By adding units to one of the numbers, show how it alters the tens and units of the other number in the pair. For example, 20 + 80: if 4 units are added to the 20, the 80 must be reduced to 70 plus 6 units to complete the 10 (20 + 4 + 70 + 6 = 20 + 70 + 4 + 6).

It is a major step when the children grasp that, if the numbers include units, the tens always add up to 90.

Copymasters
C12 Addition *Add to 100*

3 ADD MULTIPLES OF 10
C13

Ideas for whole class work
Start with a single-digit number and ask the children to add 10. Choose a different child to add each 10, building up the sequence to the nineties. Repeat the exercise, starting with different single-digit numbers. Then get them to do the same thing but adding 20 or 30 instead of 10.

Copymasters
C13 Addition *Multiples of 10* The copymaster has two sets of numbers. You need to give the children the numbers to add to each set. The numbers in set A are such that 20 can be added to each one without going over 100; in set B, 30 can be added without going over 100. They could be asked to add 10 to each number in set A and 20 to each number in set B. The following can be used with both sets: (1) add 30; (2) add 40; (3) add 20; (4) add 40; (5) add 30; (6) add 20; (7) add 10; (8) add 40; (9) add 30; (10) add 20.

4 ROUND AND APPROXIMATE
C14

Ideas for whole class work
Draw a number line labelled 0, 10, 20, 30. Give the children a two-digit number and choose a child to plot it on the line. Ask them to tell you the nearest ten. Do this several times, avoiding five in the units column to start with. Then get the children to give the nearest ten before plotting the number on the line. Move on to adding the approximated numbers, eg 21 + 38 becomes 20 + 40 = 60.

Copymasters
C14 Addition *Approximating* The children have a choice of three answers. They need to approximate the numbers to the nearest ten and add them, circling the correct number on the copymaster: (1) 31 + 12; (2) 28 + 39; (3) 17 + 22; (4) 38 + 27; (5) 11 + 13; (6) 47 + 41; (7) 29 + 73; (8) 13 + 48; (9) 32 + 57; (10) 19 + 78. The copymaster can be used again by carefully choosing the numbers to add.

LEVEL 4/5

Learning objectives
To be able to:
1. Use a variety of mental methods
2. Add several one-digit numbers
3. Practise adding two-digit numbers

1 USE A VARIETY OF MENTAL METHODS
C16-18
C20

Ideas for whole class work
The children work individually on the copymasters listed below, which provide a variety of strategies for mental calculation.

Copymasters
C16 Addition *Add nos: 9 in units column* Tell the children to add 9 to each number in set A and 19 to each number in set B, or read out the following numbers for them to add to set A and repeat for set B: (1) 9; (2) 19; (3) 29; (4) 19; (5) 39; (6) 49; (7) 29; (8) 19; (9) 49; (10) 29. The answers are all less than 100. This copymaster can be used again for the addition of other numbers.

C17 Addition *Add two 2-digit nos* Children have four sets of numbers with the units number in each set repeated. Tell the children to add 14 to set A, 15 to set B, 17 to set C, and 16 to set D. This copymaster can be used again for the addition of other numbers.

C18 Addition *Strategy: add 2-digit nos* Explain the strategy of adding the units and tens separately, then adding their sums to make the total as shown in the example.

C20 Addition *Approximating to add*

ADD SEVERAL ONE-DIGIT NUMBERS

Ideas for whole class work

1 Give the children three single-digit numbers two of which add up to 10. Encourage them to listen for pairs that make 10. For example, 4 + 7 + 6: first add 4 and 6 to make 10, then add the 7 to make 17.

2 When adding three consecutive numbers, the total is always three times the middle number, eg $4 + 5 + 6 = 3 \times 5 = 15; 5 + 6 + 7 = 3 \times 6 = 18$. This could be discovered by the children in an investigative way and then practised orally. This can also be extended to more numbers.

3 As a fun challenge for the children, see how many single-digit numbers they can remember and add.

Copymasters
C15 Addition *Add three 1-digit nos*

PRACTISE ADDING TWO-DIGIT NUMBERS

Ideas for whole class work

1 When adding any number with a 9 in the units column it can be easier for many children to add 1 to that number to make it up to a tens-only number, then add this to the second number, and finally subtract the 1, eg 29 + 34 = 30 + 34 − 1. Get the children to practise this aloud, encouraging them to explain their method. Start by adding 9 (ie add 10, subtract 1) to lots of different numbers then move on to 19.

2 Children usually try to add two-digit numbers as they stand but it is often easier to alter them first, eg 29 + 35 is the same as 30 + 34. By subtracting 1 from one number and adding it on the other number makes the sum easier. Get the children to practise changing and adding numbers. For example, 19 + 27 becomes 20 + 26; 29 + 15 becomes 30 + 14. This can be extended to subtracting and adding more than 1. For example, 18 + 34 becomes 20 + 32; 37 + 46 becomes 40 + 43.

3 Ask the children to suggest different ways of getting a 4 in the units column when adding two numbers. List them all: 0 + 4; 1 + 3; 2 + 2; 3 + 1; 4 + 0; 5 + 9; 6 + 8, and so on. Practise some quick sums to reinforce the idea that the addition always gives a 4 in the units column, eg 19 + 5, 19 + 15, 29 + 35. Many children will benefit from spotting the repeated pattern of results. If they know their number bonds to 10 and 20, mental facility speeds up with the realization that these number rules always work. This activity needs to be repeated with different unit column numbers.

Copymasters
C16 Addition *Add nos: 9 in units column*

C17 Addition *Add two 2-digit nos*

C18 Addition *Strategy: add 2-digit nos*

C19 Addition *Strategy: add 2-digit nos*

C20 Addition *Approximating to add*

Subtraction

Learning Objectives

To know:
1. Subtraction facts to 20

2. Subtract up to 100
3. How to subtract with two digits

SUBTRACTION FACTS TO 20

Ideas for whole class work

1 Subtract less than 20. Write a single-digit number on the board, then give the children another number which is bigger than the board number but less than 20. Ask them to subtract the number on the board from the second number. This can be done with different numbers. Encourage the children to look for short cuts and patterns. Start by writing an even number on the board and give them only even numbers to work with. Encourage them to notice that all the answers are even numbers.

Once they have grasped this, move on to working with all odd numbers. Finally, move on to a mixture of odd and even numbers.

2 Subtract to get a given answer. Write a single-digit number on the board, eg 8, then give the children a second number bigger than the board number but less than 20, eg 17. Ask the children to work out how much they need to subtract from the second number to get the number written on the board, eg 17 − 9 = 8 therefore 9 is

the required number. Some children find that using 10 as a stepping stone can be helpful: step one, from 17 to 10 is 7; step two, from 10 to 8 is 2. Add these to make 9.

Copymasters
C21 Subtraction *Subtract up to 20* There are four sets of numbers on the copymaster. Ask the children to subtract 5 from each number in set A, 8 from the numbers in set B, 6 from the numbers in set C, and 4 from the numbers in set D. This copymaster can be used again for subtracting other numbers.

2 SUBTRACT UP TO 100
C22-24

Ideas for whole class work
1 Count on to next whole ten. The children's ability to calculate mentally is speeded up when they make the connection that each whole ten works in the same way, ie from 7 up to 10 is 3, from 17 up to 20 is 3, and so on. For many children, this needs to be practised in order for the link to be grasped. Playing a quick-fire game where the children tell you what is required to make up a given number to the next whole ten can be fun as well as instructive, eg if you give them 34, they should reply with 6.

2 Up to a 100. When subtracting a two-digit number from 100 it is often easier to add rather than subtract. As with the addition of two two-digit numbers that include units, the sum of which is 100, where the tens of the two numbers always add up to 90, the same rule applies with subtraction. For example, 100 – 62. This can be thought of as 62 + unknown number = 100; first add 8 to 62 to make 70, then add 30. Adding the 8 and the 30 gives the unknown number. Alternatively, first add 30 to 62 to make 92 then add 8. Both methods should be practised by the children although not at the same time as this could be confusing.

Copymasters
C22 Subtraction *Count on to next whole ten*

C23 Subtraction *Subtraction and difference*

C24 Subtraction *2-digit subtraction* The children have two sets of numbers on the copymaster. You choose a number for them to put at the top of each set. They then have to find the difference between that number and each number in the set. The highest number in set A is 64. The highest number in set B is 71. Answers are given for 83 for set A and 97 for set B.

3 SUBTRACT WITH TWO DIGITS
C24

Ideas for whole class work
You need a set of cards, each marked with a single digit from 0 to 9. Have two children at the front and give each of them two cards at random. Ask them each to make a two-digit number and hold it up. The class have to work out the difference between the two numbers. You may want to ensure that one of the numbers is 0 when you first do this. Get the children to describe the method they use to work out the difference. Encourage the children to try out each others' methods and discover which one is best for them. Here are three possible ways to tackle one subtraction example, 73 – 46.

(1) Start with 46, add 4 to make 50, add 20 to make 70, then add 3 to make 73.
(2) Start with 46, add 20 to make 66, add 4 to make 70, then add 3 to make 73.
(3) Start with 73, subtract 30 to make 43, then add 3 to make 46.

Copymasters
C24 Subtraction *2-digit subtraction*

LEVEL 4/5	Learning Objectives
	To: 1. Subtract several one-digit numbers 2. Practise subtracting two-digit numbers

1 SUBTRACT SEVERAL ONE-DIGIT NUMBERS
C25

Ideas for whole class work
Start with a number, eg 20, and give three single-digit numbers for the children to subtract, eg five, two and eight. Get the children to practise with different start

numbers. Encourage them to look for pairs that make 10 and subtract them first.

Copymasters
C25 Subtraction *Subtract single digits* Give the children a start number for set A and a start number for set B (greater than 14 for set A and greater than 19 for set B to avoid negative answers). The children have to subtract single-digit numbers from the start number you give them. Answers are given for 15 and 20 respectively.

2 PRACTISE SUBTRACTING TWO-DIGIT NUMBERS

C26-30

Ideas for whole class work

1 Difference. Give the children a number, eg 14, and ask them to suggest pairs of numbers that have a difference of 14, eg 20 and 34. Repeat this exercise with other differences.

2 Write a number on the board. Ask the children to subtract that number from any number you give them and get the children to explain how they did it. Some children will use different strategies depending on the number. The following are some of the strategies you may want to practise with them.

(1) When subtracting a number with a 9 in the units column, it can be easier to make up that number to a tens-only number and subtract that, then add 1, eg $67 - 29 = 67 - 30 + 1$. Point out to the children that the units number in the answer is always one more that the units number in the start number (from which the nine-units number is subtracted), unless that is also 9.

(2) When subtracting a number in which the units figure is less than the units figure of the start number, eg $56 - 32$, it can be helpful to picture the numbers in the written form, one on top of the other, and just subtract units from units, tens from tens.

(3) When subtracting a number in which the units number is higher than the units number of the start number, it is easier to do it by adding on. Get the children to practise adding on units first as well as tens first.

3 Write a small two-digit number on the board. Choose a large two-digit number (or even a three-digit number) and make a chain by repeatedly subtracting the smaller number from it, eg start with 97 and subtract 14 which

gives the chain 97, 83, 69, 55, 41, 27, 13. Ask a different child for each answer in the chain.

4 Ask the children to close their eyes. Tell them a subtraction sum with an answer which is sometimes correct and sometimes incorrect. The children have to raise their hands if they think that the answer is correct. By having their eyes closed, it can take the pressure off those children who need longer to work it out and it also serves as a means of instant assessment for the teacher.

Copymasters

C26 Subtraction *Subtract 2-digit nos* The copymaster gives the opportunity for three games of bingo. The children need to choose five numbers in each set and circle them before you start. You then read out a subtraction sum and if the answer is one of their chosen numbers they put a line through it. Keep going until someone has crossed out all their chosen numbers. The following sums have the required answers although obviously others could be used.

Set A: $57 - 33 = 24$; $78 - 44 = 34$; $86 - 44 = 42$; $59 - 15 = 44$; $45 - 17 = 28$; $89 - 51 = 38$; $69 - 21 = 48$; $59 - 27 = 32$

Set B: $88 - 35 = 53$; $99 - 42 = 57$; $95 - 22 = 73$; $89 - 22 = 67$; $78 - 23 = 55$; $86 - 21 = 65$; $99 - 36 = 63$; $98 - 21 = 77$

Set C: $71 - 22 = 49$; $78 - 47 = 31$; $83 - 44 = 39$; $85 - 34 = 51$; $72 - 36 = 36$; $96 - 37 = 59$; $74 - 33 = 41$; $84 - 38 = 46$

C27 Subtraction *2-digit nos: check subtract*

C28 Subtraction *2-digit subtraction*

C29 Subtraction *Check by inverse operation*

C30 Subtraction *Problems using subtraction*

Multiplication

LEVEL 3

Learning Objectives

To be able to:
1. Recall two, five and 10 times tables
2. Recall three and four times tables, and up to five times five
3. Solve problems using the tables

1 RECALL 2 ×, 5 × AND 10 × TABLES

C31-33

Ideas for whole class work

1 Learn two, five and 10 times tables. Hearing the whole table repeatedly, and not simply counting in twos, fives or tens, is important for mental recall. Go through the two times table as a class. The first child says 'one times two is

two,' the second says 'two times two is four,' and so on. Keep a rhythm going. When this can be done quite easily, try going backwards through the table. Spend long enough on one table before moving on to the next. Do the same for the five and 10 times tables.

2 Multiples of 2, 5 and 10. Draw two overlapping sets on the board with a large rectangle round them. Label one the five times table and the other the two times table. Give the children a number and get them to come up and put it in the correct place. Discuss with them what is special about the numbers outside the sets (they are all odd) and the ones in the overlap (they are all in the 10 times table).

3 Mental recall of two, five and 10 times tables. Choose a table. The children have to multiply the numbers you tell them according to the table and tell you the answer. Work towards picking individuals to give you an immediate response. This exercise can be done in pairs or small groups against the clock with a pack of cards from which the kings, jacks and queens have been removed. As one child turns over the cards the other one has to multiply the number displayed on each one according to the given table and say the answer. The children have to try to improve their speed of response each time.

4 Count in twos and fives. Play Fizz Buzz. Go round the class counting from one, each child in turn saying a number but if the number is divisible by five the child has to say fizz instead of the number, eg one, two, three, four, fizz, six, seven, and so on. Do the same with twos but say buzz, eg one, buzz, three, buzz, and so on. Many children really enjoy trying to combine both: one, buzz, three, buzz, fizz, buzz, seven, and so on (10 will be fizz buzz).

Copymasters
C31 Multiplication *2 ×, 5 × and 10 × tables* The children have four sets of numbers on the copymaster. Choose a number by which they need to multiply each set. Answers are given for set A multiplied by 2, set B multiplied by 5, set C multiplied by 10, set D multiplied by 2. The copymaster can be used again with other tables.

C32 Multiplication *Recall of tables* The children have four sets of numbers on the copymaster. They need to circle all the numbers in a set which are part of a given multiplication table: set A, five times table; set B, three times table; set C, 10 times table; set D, four times table. This copymaster can be reused with other tables.

C33 Multiplication *Recall of tables* The children can be timed with this copymaster which can be reused.

2 RECALL 3 × AND 4 × UP TO 5 × 5
C32

Ideas for whole class work
1 Tables up to five times five. Draw a six-by-six grid on the board. Put the numbers 0 to 5 across the top of the grid and again down the left-hand side. Point to an empty square in the grid and ask the children to multiply the number at the top of that column by the number to the left, then write the answer in the square. Encourage the children to look for patterns and notice where answers are odd or even (odd times odd is always odd). Try doing it with the grid numbers in a random order.

Copymasters
C32 Multiplication *Recall of tables*

3 SOLVE PROBLEMS USING THE TABLES
C34

Ideas for whole class work
The children work individually with the copymaster.

Copymasters
C34 Multiplication *Solve problems with tables*

LEVEL 4/5

Learning Objectives

To be able to:
1. Know all multiplication tables up to 10 times 10
2. Use mental methods for multiplication
3. Check using inverse
4. Multiply by two-digit numbers

1 KNOW ALL MULTIPLICATION TABLES UP TO 10 × 10
C35-38

Ideas for whole class work
1 Learning six times to nine times tables. Go through the whole six times table with the class. Ask each child in turn to tell you the next multiplication in the table. Keep a rhythm going. Try going backwards through the table. Next, try dipping into the middle of a multiplication table rather than saying it in order. You say, for example, five times six is 30, then choose a child to say the next multiplication in the table.

When you have done this, try it with each child telling you the multiplication that comes before the one you have just said. Aim for speed and accuracy from the children. Concentrate on multiplying by 6, 7, 8 and 9 as these are usually what children find hardest. Make sure the children have enough practice with each multiplication table before you move on.

2 Learning the tables. Choose a table. Say three numbers, two of which are in the table and one of which is not. The children have to pick out the odd one. Some children enjoy the challenge of finding the odd one out without being told to which table the others belong, although there may be two possible odd ones out depending on the table chosen by the child.

3 Mental recall of tables. Choose a multiplication table and tell the children a number between 0 and 10. The children could be divided into groups so that each group could be given different tables. They have to multiply the number you tell them according to the given multiplication table.

4 Mental recall of tables. This is for children who know their tables quite well. Choose two multiplication tables, preferably two that are close together. Tell the children a number that appears in one of the tables. They have to give you the next number, the lower of the two possible choices from one of the chosen tables. For example, if the seven times and eight times tables are chosen and you say 35, the next number would be 40 (rather than 42).

Copymasters
C35 Multiplication *Practise tables* The children have four sets of numbers on the copymaster. Give them numbers by which they multiply each set. Answers are given for set A multiply by 3, set B multiply by 6, set C multiply by 4, set D multiply by 9. The copymaster can be used again with other tables.

C36 Multiplication *Practise tables* The children have a multiplication grid on the copymaster. You need to choose three multiplication tables for the children to practise. Different children could be given different tables. The children can be timed with this copymaster which can be used again.

C37 Multiplication *Recognize nos in tables*

C38 Multiplication *Recall of tables*

2 MENTAL METHODS OF MULTIPLICATION

This Learning Objective is covered by the other Learning Objectives in this topic.

3 CHECK USING INVERSE
C39

Ideas for whole class work
The children work individually with the copymaster.

Copymasters
C39 Multiplication *Use inverse*

4 MULTIPLY BY TWO-DIGIT NUMBERS
C40

Ideas for whole class work
Being able to multiply by multiples of 10 is invaluable for estimating answers. Show the children that $2 \times 40 = 2 \times 4 \times 10$. Use this to split up and work out other simple multiplications, eg 4×60, 3×70, 6×80. Then move on to two two-digit numbers, eg $60 \times 30 = 6 \times 3 \times 10 \times 10 = 18 \times 100$.

Copymasters
C40 Multiplication *Multiply by 2-digit nos*

Division

LEVEL **3**	**Learning Objectives** To be able to: 1. Recall mentally two, five and 10 times tables	2. Use knowledge of multiplication tables for division 3. Divide with remainders 4. Use division to solve problems

1 RECALL 2 ×, 5 × AND 10 × TABLES
C41-42

Ideas for whole class work
Recognizing numbers in multiplication tables. Choose a multiplication table. Tell the children a number and ask them to tell you whether it is in that multiplication table. You may wish to get children to close their eyes and raise their hands rather than answer verbally; this is a good assessment of both speed and accuracy in a simple and non-threatening way.

Copymasters
C41 Division *Recall nos in tables* There are two sets of numbers on the copymaster. Ask the children whether they can divide the numbers of one set by 5 and the numbers of the other set by 2, telling them to ring the correct answer (yes or no) on the copymaster. Answers are given for set A divided by 2 and set B divided by 5.

C42 Division *Recall nos in tables* The copymaster has two pairs of overlapping ovals, each oval representing a set of numbers that can be divided by a given number (as indicated on the copymaster). You tell the children numbers and they have to write them in the correct place.

The top sets are multiples of 2 and 5. Suggested numbers include 4, 16, 15, 18, 35, 20, 45, 12, 10, and 5. The lower sets are multiples of 5 and 10. Suggested numbers include 20, 35, 50, 15, 10, 25, 5, and 40. Whether you introduce numbers higher than 50 will depend on the children's grasp of multiples of 5. The numbers 60, 70, and so on are obviously supposed to be in the overlapping section but will not have been learned as part of the five times table.

remainder of 1 when divided by 2. List them on the board and encourage the children to notice that they are all odd. Discuss why this is the case (all the numbers in the two times table are even so one more is bound to make them odd). Next, try doing the same thing for the five times table. The numbers in the five times table all end in 5 or 0 so if there is a remainder of 1 they will end in 1 or 6.

Children will often be able to make predictions about the 10 times table without much guidance as the remainder is always the number in the units column.

Copymasters
C43 Division *Division and remainders*

2 C43 USE KNOWLEDGE OF MULTIPLICATION TABLES FOR DIVISION

Ideas for whole class work
Try chanting the division tables, eg five divided by five is one, 10 divided by five is two, and so on. Multiplication tables need to be quite well known in order for the children to manage this. Try choosing individuals to tell you the next line of the division table. Repeat the exercise for other multiplication tables.

Copymasters
C43 Division *Division and remainders*

3 C43 DIVIDE WITH REMAINDERS

Ideas for whole class work
Ask the children to suggest numbers which would have a

4 C44 USE DIVISION TO SOLVE PROBLEMS

Ideas for whole class work
Set some problems in the context of your class. The following are examples.

(1) There are 30 of you here today and I want five equal groups. How many will there be in each group?
(2) There are 33 here today. How could I group you?
(3) There are 11 players in the football team and we can fit four in each car to get to an away match. How many full cars will there be with how many players left over?
(4) There are 14 players in a netball match. How many oranges will we need and into how many pieces should we cut them? How many pieces are left over?

Copymasters
C44 Division *Division to solve problems*

| LEVEL 4/5 | **Learning Objectives**

To:
1. Recall multiplication facts mentally | 2. Use multiplication facts up to 10 times 10 for division
3. Begin to develop tests for divisibility
4. Divide multiples of 10 to give whole number answers |

1 C45 C50 RECALL MULTIPLICATION FACTS MENTALLY

Ideas for whole class work
Choose a multiplication table. Tell the children a number and ask them whether it is in that multiplication table. You may wish to get the children to close their eyes and raise their hands rather than answer verbally. This is a good assessment of both speed and accuracy in a simple and non-threatening way.

Copymasters
C45 Division *Recall of tables* There are four sets of numbers on the copymaster. Tell the children to ring the numbers in each set which can be divided exactly by the number you give them. In set A, some numbers are divisible by 6, some by 7. In set B, some numbers are divisible by 8, some by 6. In set C, some numbers are divisible by 9, some by 7. In set D, some numbers are divisible by 8, some by 9.

C50 Division *Recall of tables*

2 USE MULTIPLICATION FACTS UP TO 10 × 10 FOR DIVISION

C46
C49-50

Ideas for whole class work

1 Chant the division tables. Multiplication tables need to be quite well known in order for the children to manage this. Try asking different children in turn to tell you the next division in the table. Repeat the exercise with other tables.

2 Write some selected numbers on the board, eg 13, 16, 26, 30, 33, and ask questions, such as, which numbers would have a remainder of 1 when divided by 4. Do the same thing with other numbers. Write 13, 17, 19, 25, 35, 37, 49, 53 on the board and ask which of them would have a remainder of 1 when divided by 6. Write 13, 15, 22, 34, 36, 43, 51, 57 on the board and ask which of them would have a remainder of 1 when divided by 7.

Copymasters

C46 Division *Division with remainders* Tell the children to circle numbers which have a remainder of 1 when divided by 6 and draw a square round numbers which have a remainder of 2 when divided by 8. The copymaster can be reused for numbers divided by 5 with remainder 1, divided by 4 with remainder 1, and divided by 7 with remainder 1.

C49 Division *Solving problems*

C50 Division *Recall of tables*

3 BEGIN TO DEVELOP TESTS FOR DIVISIBILITY

C47

Ideas for whole class work

Check that the children know that numbers divisible by 2

are all even numbers and have 0, 2, 4, 6, or 8 in the units column; that numbers divisible by 5 all have a 5 or a 0 in the units column; and that numbers divisible by 10 all have a 0 in the units column. Use these tests on several numbers. For example, is 75 divisible by 5? Yes, because it has a 5 in the units column. Is 80 divisible by 2, 5 and 10? Yes, because it has a 0 in the units column.

List some numbers divisible by 3. Help the children to notice that the digit sum of each of the numbers is 3, 6, or 9, eg 9 × 3 = 27 and 2 + 7 = 9, 7 × 3 = 21 and 2 + 1 = 3. All numbers which are divisible by 3 fit this pattern. Test it out on several numbers. For example, is 135 divisible by 3? Yes, because 1 + 3 + 5 = 9. The digit sum of all numbers divisible by 9 is 9. Use this to check for numbers which are multiples of 9. For example, the smallest multiple of 9 with three digits; the next multiple of 9 after...

Copymasters

C47 Division *Nos divisible by 3, 8, 6 & 9* The children need to understand how a Carroll diagram works before attempting this copymaster.

4 DIVIDE MULTIPLES OF 10 TO GIVE WHOLE NUMBER ANSWERS

C48

Ideas for whole class work

Show the children that 120 ÷ 4 = 10 × 12 ÷ 4 = 10 × 3 = 30. Show them how multiplication tables can help to divide other multiples of 10. For example, 420 ÷ 6 = 10 × 42 ÷ 6. Practise this with lots of numbers. Next, move on to sums such as 4200 ÷ 6 or 4200 ÷ 60.

Copymasters

C48 Division *Multiples of 10: whole nos*

Number patterns

LEVEL **3**

Learning Objectives

To be able to:
1. Use halving and doubling

2. Recognize and continue number patterns
3. Use simple input-output machines
4. Inverse operations

1 USE HALVING AND DOUBLING

C51

Ideas for whole class work

1 Start with a low number. Ask the children to double it.

Get a child to explain how they did it. Lots of children double numbers by adding the number to itself but in order to cope with halving it is better if they think of it as multiplying by 2. Practise doubling other low numbers. Next, start to build doubling chains, eg 3, 6, 12, 24, or 2, 4, 8, 16, 32. Encourage the children to notice that all the numbers are even except the number they start with, which may be odd.

2 Give the children numbers, 1–30 for example, and tell them to find the children who have numbers in their doubling/halving chain (1, 2, 4, 8, 16 go together; 5, 10, 20 go together, and so on). Ask them to look at the numbers which are not part of a chain and discuss why they are not. For example, odd numbers higher than 15 cannot be exactly halved and doubling them makes numbers over 30.

3 Tell the children a number and tell them to double it if it is odd but to halve it if it is even. Choose individuals to answer each time or go round the class asking each child in turn. This simple activity revises odd and even numbers and aims for speed and accuracy with doubling and halving.

Copymasters
C51 Number Patterns *Doubling and halving*

2 RECOGNIZE AND CONTINUE NUMBER PATTERNS
C52

Ideas for whole class work
The children will need calculators. Tell them to enter 2 + 3 = (on some calculators the addition sign will need to be pressed twice to make a constant function). The display will show 5. Now tell them to press equals twice more which will give 8, then 11. Ask the children to describe the pattern of adding 3. Ask them to predict the next two numbers, then to press equals twice more to see if they are right. Next, try starting with other numbers and using different constant functions. This method can also be used to reinforce the fact that multiplication tables are made by repeated addition.

Copymasters
C52 Number Patterns *Recognize/continue patterns*

3 USE SIMPLE INPUT-OUTPUT MACHINES
C53

Ideas for whole class work
Write a function on the board, eg +4. Whatever number you give to the children, they have to perform that function and tell you the answer. Most calculators can be programmed so tell them to enter + 4 = 0. Next, they press any number followed by = and the calculator will add 4 to it.

Tell them not to clear the display but to enter the next number and to continue doing this. The children can play in pairs. The first player programs the calculator with a 'hidden function' and the second one enters any three numbers to try to work out what the calculator is adding.

Next, get the children to program their calculators to subtract; tell them to press − 2 = 0.

Copymasters
C53 Number Patterns *Input-output machines* There are four sets of numbers on the copymaster. Choose the function to be performed by the children on each set, eg add 2. Answers are given for set A, add 4; set B, add 3; set C, subtract 5; set D, subtract 4. This copymaster can be used several times with different functions.

4 INVERSE OPERATIONS
C54

Ideas for whole class work
The children work individually on the copymaster.

Copymasters
C54 Number Patterns *Inverse operations* There are 10 questions, each with start numbers that are the same as the finish numbers. Give the children the function to perform in the first box. They work out the middle number and the function which gives them the finish number. This copymaster can be used again with other functions.

LEVEL 4/5

Learning Objectives

To be able to:
1. Know factors, multiples and square numbers

2. Use simple formulae
3. Use inverse to find missing numbers
4. Continue and describe numbers patterns
5. Use input output machines

1 KNOW FACTORS, MULTIPLES AND SQUARE NUMBERS
C55

Ideas for whole class work
Choose a number and get the children to tell you as much as they can about it using the terms factor, multiple or square. For example, 9 is a multiple of 3, a factor of 27, and the square of 3. You could do this as a challenge such as 'Who can think of five statements in 1 minute?' or even get the children to write down their ideas and share them.

Copymasters
C55 Number Patterns *List factors in pairs*

2 USE SIMPLE FORMULAE

Ideas for whole class work
Write a rule on the board, eg × 2 and − 1. Give the children some numbers. They use the rule to find the outputs. Work up in order, so the first child takes 1, the second takes 2, and so on. Next try writing the rule as 2n − 1.

Copymasters
None.

3 USE INVERSE TO FIND MISSING NUMBERS
C56
C60

Ideas for whole class work
The children work individually on the copymaster.

Copymasters
C56 Number Patterns *Use inverse functions* Each question has start and finish numbers that are the same. Give the functions to perform in the first two boxes. The children then work out the missing numbers and functions to give the finish numbers. Use again with different functions.

C60 Number Patterns *Think of a number*

4 CONTINUE AND DESCRIBE NUMBER PATTERNS
C57-58

Ideas for whole class work
1 Choose a function, eg add 3, and a start number, eg 2.

Ask each child in turn for the next number. Then, give the children different start numbers and different functions. You could give each child a number from 1 to 30 and ask them to stand in the sequence and say their number as it comes up.

2 Repeat with a different function and start number. Ask for, say, the fourth number in the sequence, or the next number after 17, or whether 24 is in the sequence.

3 Give the children start and finish numbers that fulfill a rule you choose. Ask them to suggest what the rule is.

After a few suggestions, give the children other start and finish numbers that satisfy your rule. Ask them to check their suggestions against the numbers. You will then need to give a third pair for the children to check their choice. This activity helps to prepare the children for writing algebraic rules at a higher level.

Copymasters
C57 Number Patterns *Patterns and rules*

C58 Number Patterns *Continue/describe patterns*

5 USE INPUT-OUTPUT MACHINES
C59

Ideas for whole class work
The children work individually on the copymaster.

Copymasters
C59 Number Patterns *Use input-output machines* There are four sets of numbers on the copymaster. Give them one-step functions for sets A and B and two-step functions for sets C and D. This copymaster can be reused with different functions. Answers are given for set A multiply by 2; set B multiply by 3; set C multiply by 3, subtract 2; set D subtract 2, multiply by 4.

Fractions

Learning Objectives

To be able to:
1. Understand fractions up to a tenth
2. Add or subtract fractions with the same denominator
3. Find simple fractions of amounts
4. Find equal parts
5. Shade simple fractions

LEVEL 3

1 UNDERSTAND FRACTIONS UP TO A TENTH
C61
C64

Ideas for whole class work
The link between what the fraction is called, the denominator and the number of equal parts in the fraction is crucial for further understanding. Play a quick-fire game to reinforce this. Say, for example, 'five equal parts, take one of them' and choose a child to reply 'one-fifth'. Ask another child to write the fraction on the board.

When the children are secure in the knowledge that the denominator is the number of equal parts in the fraction, start changing the numerator.

Copymasters
C61 Fractions *Shade simple fractions* The copymaster has various shapes divided into equal parts. Tell the children the amount to shade: (1) quarter, (2) sixth, (3) third, (4) eighth, (5) quarter, (6) sixth, (7) third, (8) eighth. This copymaster can be reused by asking the children to shade different amounts.

C64 Fractions *Fractions up to a tenth*

2 ADD OR SUBTRACT FRACTIONS WITH THE SAME DENOMINATOR
C62

Ideas for whole class work

1 Another stepping stone in understanding fractions is grasping the fact that if the numerator equals the denominator then it makes a whole one. Play Making One with the children. Give them a fraction and ask a child to make it up to a whole one.

Move on to Making One in two steps. You need to be careful that the fractions you choose will allow two children to add to it before it makes a whole one. For example, if you say two-fifths, the first child replies with one-fifth and the second child must say two-fifths to make it up to a whole one. The first child must not make a whole one with their addition.

2 You will need coloured squares or tiles such as Polydron or Clixi for this exercise. Make a strip of three squares using two colours, eg one blue and two green. Establish with the children what fraction of the strip each square represents, in this case, one-third. Ask what fraction green represents. Each square is one-third, so one-third add one-third is two-thirds.

Repeat this for strips of different lengths. Each time, build up the answer by adding each square. Repeating the additions out loud reinforces the addition of fractions with the same denominator.

Copymasters
C62 Fractions *Add: same denominator*

3 FIND SIMPLE FRACTIONS OF AMOUNTS
C63

Ideas for whole class work

Make two groups of children, eight in one group and six in the other. Ask which has more children: half of the group of six or quarter of the group of eight. Discuss with the children how to find each amount by dividing the group and emphasize again the link between the denominator of the fraction and the number of equal parts. Repeat this for other group sizes or use, for example, piles of cubes, lengths of lines, amounts of money.

Copymasters
C63 Fractions *Equal parts and fractions* The copymaster has lines of various lengths on it. Tell the children what fraction to find. You may want to start by finding a half of each one before moving on to the following suggestions: (1) quarter/half, (2) third/sixth, (3) sixth/third, (4) fifth/tenth, (5) quarter/eighth.

This copymaster can be reused to find fractions such as two-thirds of 6 cm, three-fifths of 10 cm, and so on.

4 FIND EQUAL PARTS
C63

Ideas for whole class work

You need a piece of string about a metre long and a pair of scissors. Hold up the string and ask for a volunteer to cut it in half. Discuss how they know the right place to cut it. Stress that the parts must be equal and that you end up with two parts. Write on the board 'half of the string: two equal parts'.

Repeat the exercise with another piece of string and thirds. Explain that thirds are three equal parts and ask for a volunteer to cut the string into thirds. Stress that you have three equal parts. Write on the board 'one-third of the string: three equal parts'.

Repeat the exercise with other simple fractions.

Encourage the children to notice the link between what the fraction is called, the denominator and the number of equal parts in the fraction.

Copymasters
C63 Fractions *Equal parts and fractions*

5 SHADE SIMPLE FRACTIONS
C61

Ideas for whole class work
The children work individually on the copymaster.

Copymasters
C61 Fractions *Shade simple fractions*

Learning Objectives

To be able to:
1. Use simple fractions
2. Find fractions of amounts
3. Order fractions
4. Understand equivalence of fractions

1 USE SIMPLE FRACTIONS

This Learning Objective is covered by the other Learning Objectives in this topic.

2 FIND FRACTIONS OF AMOUNTS
C65-66
C70

Ideas for whole class work

1 You may want the children to use calculators as this reinforces the link between fractions and division. Divide the class into three groups and tell them that you want group one to find a half, group two to find a third and group three to find a quarter of each number you give them, eg 24 (12, 8, 6), 36 (18, 12, 9), 48 (24, 16, 12). As they feed back the answers, get them to explain how they found the each amount. You could write the answers on the board and encourage the children to spot patterns.

2 This is a quick-fire consolidation of the link between fractions and division. Ask the children for numbers of which they could find a third. List them on the board and note the fact that they are all exactly divisible by three. Repeat this for other fractions.

Copymasters

C65 Fractions *Find fractions of amounts*

C66 Fractions *Find fractions of amounts*

C70 Fractions *Find fractions of amounts*

3 ORDER FRACTIONS
C67

Ideas for whole class work

1 The easiest way to compare fractions is to use a number and find the given fractions of that number. For example, is two-fifths bigger or smaller than one-third? Fifteen is a number of which you can find thirds and fifths; one-third of 15 is 5, two-fifths of 15 is 6; hence, two-fifths is clearly bigger than one-third.

Compare other fractions in the same way. Start with fractions where the common multiple is not too large, eg fifths and quarters, thirds and quarters, sixths and quarters.

2 Write three digits on the board and ask the children to give all the possible fractions that can be made with those digits, eg 2, 3, 5 will make two-thirds, two-fifths, three-halves, three-fifths, five-halves and five-thirds (you may want to allow two-halves, three-thirds and five-fifths as well). Get the children to order the fractions, putting the smallest first. Rewrite three-halves as one and a half.

Repeat this for other sets of digits. You could give different sets of digits to different groups.

Copymasters

C67 Fractions *Order fractions* There are four sets of fractions on the copymaster. Give them a fraction for each set and they compare their fractions with the one you give them, deciding whether it is smaller or bigger each time. Answers are given for set A one-third, set B seven-tenths, set C two-thirds, set D one-quarter. This copymaster can be reused with other fractions.

4 EQUIVALENCE OF FRACTIONS
C68-69

Ideas for whole class work

Find a half of several numbers and list the number and its half on the board. Rewrite them as equivalent fractions and note that the numerator is always half of the denominator. Although this may seem very obvious, it is worth making it explicit to the children. Do the same thing for thirds of numbers and this time note that the numerator is one third of the denominator. Ask the children for fractions equivalent to a quarter, a fifth, and a tenth, then move on to fractions where the numerator is greater than one.

Copymasters

C68 Fractions *Equivalent fractions* The copymaster has four sections labelled one-half, one-third, one-quarter and one-fifth. Verbally give the children fractions for them to write next to the fraction to which they are equivalent: three-sixths, two-eighths, two-tenths, two-sixths, four-eighths, four-twentieths, five-tenths, three-fifteenths, three-ninths, three-twelfths, two-quarters, four-sixteenths.

C69 Fractions *Equivalent fractions*

Decimals

LEVEL 3

Learning Objectives

To be able to:
1. Recognize and interpret tenths as decimals
2. Use decimal point
3. Order simple decimals
4. Round decimal numbers to the nearest whole one
5. Add and subtract tenths

1 RECOGNIZE AND INTERPRET TENTHS AS DECIMALS

Ideas for whole class work
You need a calculator between two children. Tell them to enter 0·1 and add (+) on their calculators (on some calculators the addition sign will need to be pressed twice to make a constant function). Tell them to press = several times, observing closely what happens in the display: which digit changes every time they press equals; what happens after 0·9. Ask them to explain why. Next, get them to enter 0·2 and add (+) to start with and again look closely at the display as they press equals, and to describe what is happening and explain why.

Copymasters
None.

2 USE DECIMAL POINT

Ideas for whole class work
Draw a number line on the board from 0 to 1. Plot an arrow on the number line, eg at 0·7, and get the children to estimate the number it represents. Discuss why they may or may not be right. You may find it helpful to identify the number halfway as 0·5. Plot arrows for different numbers, then try moving on to new number lines, eg from 2 to 4.

Copymasters
None.

3 ORDER SIMPLE DECIMALS

C71

Ideas for whole class work
Draw a number line on the board from 0 to 1. Ask one child to give you a number between 0 and 1, and tell them to plot an arrow on the line where they think it will go.

Get the other children to guess what the number is.

Choose another number and ask the children which side of the first number you should plot it and to explain why. Extend the number line so it goes from nought to three and get the children to plot numbers such as 1·6, 2·8. Each time, discuss its position compared to other numbers.

Copymasters
C71 Decimals *Order simple decimals* Give the children three numbers to plot on each number line. You could use the following numbers but this copymaster can be used again with different numbers for the children to plot.

Line 1: plot 0·8, 1·5 and 0·2; **Line 2:** plot 1·9, 0·9 and 1·1
Line 3: plot 2·5, 2·4 and 3·1; **Line 4:** plot 6·8, 6·0 and 5·9
Line 5: plot 7·3, 7·6 and 8·2; **Line 6:** plot 4·4, 3·3 and 3·6

4 ROUND DECIMALS TO THE NEAREST WHOLE ONE

C72

Ideas for whole class work
Draw a number line on the board from 0 to 1. Plot an arrow on the line, eg at 0·7, and get the children to estimate the number it represents. Discuss why, for example, 0·3 would not be a good estimate and use the language 'nearer to nought' and 'nearer to one'. Next, extend the number line and plot other arrows. Each time, discuss possible values for the arrows and the whole number to which the decimal is nearer.

Copymasters
C72 Decimals *To nearest whole number*

5 ADD AND SUBTRACT TENTHS

C73-74

Ideas for whole class work
You may want to use calculators for this activity to start with so that the children can actually see the numbers changing. Get the children to add 0·1 to various simple decimals. Avoid having a 9 in the tenths column until the children get to grips with the fact that the number in the

units column stays the same and the number in the tenths column increases by 1 when you add a tenth.

Get the children to subtract 0·1 from simple decimals. Next, focus on the numbers in which the units number changes as well as the tenths, eg 2·9, 3·9, 4·9, and so on when adding 0·1, and 3·0, 5·0, 8·0 when subtracting 0·1. Then, move on to adding and subtracting 0·2, 0·3, and so on.

Copymasters

C73 Decimals *Add/subtract tenths & units* The copymaster has two sets of numbers. Tell the children to add a tenth or a unit to, or subtract a tenth or a unit from, each number in the sets. Answers are given for set A, add a tenth; set B, add a unit. This copymaster can be used again with different instructions.

C74 Decimals *Add and subtract*

Learning Objectives

To be able to:
1. Order decimals with two decimal places
2. Add and subtract decimals
3. Multiply and divide by 10, 100 and 1000
4. Understand place value in decimals

1 ORDER DECIMALS WITH TWO DECIMAL PLACES

C75-76

Ideas for whole class work

1 Prepare some cards in advance with numbers less than 10 written on them, with all the numbers to two decimal places. Get one of the children to come out to the front and hold a card for all to see, eg 3·56. Get another child to show them another card, eg 4·56. Ask them to tell you if the second number is more or less than the first number. Discuss with them which side of the first child the second child should stand.

Give other children cards and each time ask the class to help them to stand in the correct place for the numbers to be in order. You can make this activity harder or easier according to the numbers you write on the cards.

Next, introduce numbers to one decimal place and discuss whether they are bigger or smaller than the numbers to two decimal places; eg is 3·50 bigger or smaller than 3·38? Plotting the numbers on a number line or converting them to money can help the children to order mixed decimals.

2 Choose a start number, eg 1·34, and choose an amount to add to it, eg 0·10 (you may wish to omit the second decimal place 0). Go round the class building up the sequence 1·34, 1·44, 1·54, and so on. Emphasize which digits are changing and which are not. Do this with other start numbers and functions. Calculators can be used to reinforce which digits change.

3 Get the children to give you numbers that satisfy given limits, eg bigger than 3·6 but smaller than 4·1. Move on to numbers closer together, eg 5·7 and 5·8. Plotting the numbers on a number line will help some children to give numbers using two decimal places.

4 Write two numbers on the board, eg 3 and 7 and get the children to tell you the number that is halfway between them. Do this for other whole numbers. Move on to consecutive numbers, eg 4 and 5, and again find the halfway numbers. Plotting the numbers on a number line

can help some children. Get the children to try finding the halfway numbers between tenths, eg halfway between 2·4 and 2·5.

Copymasters

C75 Decimals *Order decimals* The copymaster has six different number lines on it. Get the children to plot and write down either numbers that you give them or numbers which satisfy certain limits.

Line 1: plot a number > 0·20 < 0·60
Line 2: plot a number > 3·40 < 3·70
Line 3: plot a number > 5·50 < 5·60
Line 4: plot a number > 7·20 < 7·30
Line 5: plot a number > 0·45 < 0·50
Line 6: plot a number > 1·65 < 1·70

This copymaster can be reused with other limits.

C76 Decimals *Order decimals*

2 ADD AND SUBTRACT DECIMALS

C77

Ideas for whole class work

Get the children to list some pairs of numbers that add up to 1. Start with one decimal place if necessary. List the pairs and encourage the children to notice the link with adding numbers to 100 (a 100 hundredths make a whole one, eg 33 + 67 = 100 and 0·33 + 0·67 = 1). Encourage the children to notice that the numbers in the hundredths column always add up to ten-hundredths and that the numbers in the tenths column always add up to nine-tenths.

Copymasters

C77 Decimals *Add and subtract decimals* Give the children two functions for each question. You may want them to perform the same operations in each question or you could give them different functions.

Answers are given for add 0·20 as the first function and add 1·00 as the second.

3 MULTIPLY AND DIVIDE BY 10, 100 AND 1000
C78-79

Ideas for whole class work
The children work individually on the copymasters.

Copymasters
C78 Decimals *Multiply/divide: 10, 100, 1000*

C79 Decimals *Add/subtract/multiply/divide*

4 UNDERSTAND PLACE VALUE IN DECIMALS
C80

Ideas for whole class work
The children work individually on the copymaster. This Learning Objective is also covered by other Learning Objectives in this topic.

Copymasters
C80 Decimals *Place value in decimals*

Money

LEVEL 3

Learning Objectives
To be able to:
1. Use decimal notation in money
2. Make up amounts using coins
3. Add, subtract, multiply and divide
4. Work out change

1 USE DECIMAL NOTATION IN MONEY
C81

Ideas for whole class work
The children work individually on the copymaster.

Copymasters
C81 Money *Decimal notation in money*

2 MAKE UP AMOUNTS USING COINS
C82

Ideas for whole class work
1 Make up amounts using coins. Have a group of children at the front of the class holding cards with coin values on them. You may start with, for example, two children holding cards with 1p on them, two children holding cards with 2p on them and one child holding a card with 5p on it. Say an amount to the children and ask them to tell you which children from the group at the front would make up that amount. Show the children how to start with the largest coin values and work down. For example, for 8p first ask how many fives there are in 8p (one with 3p left). Then ask them how many twos there are in 3p (one with 1p left).

Move on to using 10p and 20p values and ask them about larger amounts. This can be great fun when played in teams. Each team has a selection of 'coin children' and the first team to select the right 'coin children' for the given amount gets a point.

2 Make up amounts using coins and simple division. You can either choose a value of a coin for all the children to work with or give a number of groups different coin values to work with. Tell them an amount of money, eg 60p, and ask the children to work out how many of their coins it would take to make that amount. If groups are given different amounts, you need to be careful about what you ask them to work on or warn the children that the answer may not be an exact number of their coins.

Copymasters
C82 Money *Make up amounts* The copymaster has spaces for amounts of money and numbers of coins. Give the children the amount of money for each question and they work out how that amount could be made up using the suggested coins. Answers are given for: (1) 12p; (2) 27p; (3) 11p; (4) 18p; (5) 36p; (6) 78p (7) 83p; (8) 99p. The copymaster can be reused with different amounts.

3 ADD, SUBTRACT, MULTIPLY AND DIVIDE
C83

Ideas for whole class work
1 Do simple calculations using addition and subtraction. Write an amount of money on the board, preferably a small amount, and ask each child in turn to add it to the previous figure, building up a sequence, eg 5p, 15p, 25p, 35p, and so on. Repeat this with different amounts. Next, get the children to keep subtracting a given amount from £1, eg 4p: £1, 96p, 92p, 88p, and so on. This is quite hard and you may need to keep to subtracting multiples of 10 or 5.

2 Do simple calculations using multiplication. Write the value of a coin on the board and tell the children how many of these you have. Ask them to work out how much money that is. You may want to give groups of children different values of coins.

Copymasters
C83 Money *Add and subtract amounts* The copymaster has two sets of money on it. Tell the children to add a given amount to set A and subtract another given amount from set B. Answers are given for set A add 10p, set B subtract 20p. This copymaster can be reused by giving the children different amounts to add and subtract.

4 WORK OUT CHANGE
C84

Ideas for whole class work
The better the children are at working out pairs that make

100, the easier it is for them to work out change from £1. Using coins, you may want to show them the pairing of multiples of 10 that make 100, eg 10p + 90p, 20p + 80p, then show them how, if one of these tens is used as units, there are always nine 10p coins left.

Adding up to the next whole ten is the most common way to work out change. Tell the children amounts and ask them how much is needed to make the next whole ten, then how much is needed to make £1. Work up to doing this in one step.

Get the children to work out change from £5. Write some pairs of amounts on the board that make £5, eg £1.63 and £3.37, £2.14 and £2.86, and so on. Encourage the children to notice that the pounds always add up to £4, the tens always add up to 90p and the units always add up to 10p. Get the children to use this information to practise working out change from £5.

Copymasters
C84 Money *Work out change*

LEVEL 4/5

Learning Objectives

To be able to:
1. Work out change
2. Add, subtract, multiply and divide
3. Solve problems using money
4. Make up amounts using coins

1 WORK OUT CHANGE

Ideas for whole class work
Write on the board some pairs of amounts that make £10 (you could start with £5 for revision). Encourage the children to notice that the pounds always add up to £9, the tens always add up to 90p and the units always add up to 10p. When the children latch on to this simple pattern, it really speeds up their working out of change.

Copymasters
None.

2 ADD, SUBTRACT, MULTIPLY AND DIVIDE
C85-88

Ideas for whole class work
1 Calculations using addition. Lots of prices include 99p so it is useful for the children to practise working with this amount. The strategy is the same idea as for adding 9p. It is easier to add £1 and then subtract 1p than to try to add 99p. So £2.50 + £1.99 becomes £2.50 + £2.00 which equals £4.50, then subtract 1p to get £4.49. Get the children to practise this with many different amounts.

Next, give the children amounts that include 98p, the strategy for which is to add £1, then subtract 2p.

2 Do calculations using multiplication. This is based on the idea described above but involves multiplying given amounts that include 99p. If you have four lots of 99p then that is the same as four lots of £1 subtract four lots of 1p. So $6 \times £1.99$ is the same as $6 \times £2 - (6 \times 1p)$ which is $£12.00 - £0.06 = £11.94$. Get the children to practise this for lots of different amounts and multipliers.

Get the children to multiply amounts that include 98p. The strategy for this is to subtract 2p for each amount, eg $5 \times £4.98$ is the same as $5 \times £5$ subtract $5 \times 2p$ which is $£25.00 - £0.10 = £24.90$.

Copymasters
C85 Money *Addition and subtraction* The copymaster has two sets of numbers on it. Give the children amounts to add to set A and to subtract from set B. Answers are given for set A add 50p, set B subtract 70p. Use again by giving the children different amounts to add and subtract.

C86 Money *Addition and subtraction* The copymaster has two sets of numbers on it. Give the children amounts to make each sum of money up to. Answers are given for set A, £8.50; and set B, £9.25. This copymaster could be used to practise making up amounts to the next whole number of pounds or up to £10.

C87 Money *Multiplication and division*

C88 Money *Multiply/add: 90p amounts*

3 SOLVE PROBLEMS USING MONEY

C87-89

Ideas for whole class work
The children work individually on the copymasters.

Copymasters
C87 Money *Multiplication and division*

C88 Money *Multiply/add: 90p amounts*

C89 Money *Solve money problems*

4 MAKE UP AMOUNTS USING COINS

C90

Ideas for whole class work
1 Get the children to tell you the minimum number of coins or notes needed to make up a given amount. The children should start with the coin or note with the largest value possible, eg to make £18.53 start with a £10 note, then a £5 note, three £1 coins, a 50p piece, a 2p piece and a 1p piece. Get the children to practise this for a variety of amounts up to £20 or more. Make sure that the children know the value of the notes and coins in general use.

2 Use copymaster C90 for this challenge. Start by choosing a target amount less than £5 and tell the children to write it in the target column. Next, either throw three dice to generate random numbers or select three numbers. The children then need to decide into which columns to place the numbers in order to get a total as near to the target as possible.

Each number must be used only once and only one number can be placed in any one column. The children score two points for exactly getting the target amount and one point for being within 2p of it. Obviously, the rules can be adapted. You may want to use numbers up to 10 or choose more than three numbers.

Copymasters
C90 Money *Game sheet*

Time

LEVEL **3**	**Learning Objectives**

To be able to:
1. Tell the time using analogue and digital time
2. Estimate time
3. Know and use the order of the months
4. Use am and pm
5. Work out duration

1 TELL THE TIME USING ANALOGUE AND DIGITAL TIME

C91

Ideas for whole class work
You need a large analogue clock. Children find it easier to change from analogue to digital time if they have an idea of intervals of 5 that add to 60. It is easier to change '25 to' into '35 minutes past' if they know that 25 + 35 = 60. Or, using the five times table – the hand points to the 7; 7 × 5 = 35. Put the clock at one of the quarter hours and ask the children to say and write the time in different ways. Repeat with different times, moving on to 5-minute intervals.

Copymasters
C91 Time *Tell the time: analogue/digital*

2 ESTIMATE TIME

Ideas for whole class work
Ask the children to do a simple activity (do not bring time to their attention). Time them, then get them to estimate how long it took. Ask them to estimate how many times they can write their name in 1 minute. Get them to do it. Do other 1-minute activities to improve estimation skills.

Copymasters
None.

3 KNOW AND USE THE ORDER OF THE MONTHS
C92

Ideas for whole class work
Tell the children a month and ask which comes next. Do this for several months. Then ask them for the month before. Move on to questions like which month is three months after March and which is five months before May.

Make sure that they learn the numbers of the months; January is 1. Show them how you can use the numbers to work out how long it is between months, eg February is month 2, three months after that is month 5, which is May.

Copymasters
C92 Time *Know and use the months*

4 USE AM AND PM

Ideas for whole class work
Draw on the board a time line from midnight to midnight. Use colour to show where am and pm are. Get the children to come up and plot on the time line events such as 'eat breakfast' saying whether the time is am or pm. Write the times next to the events plotted in the form 8:15 am.

Copymasters
None.

5 WORK OUT DURATION
C93-94

Ideas for whole class work
Write a length of time on the board, eg half an hour. Give the children various times and ask them to give you the time half an hour later; to start with, give them simple times on the hour, half past the hour, and quarter to and quarter past the hour. Do this with lots of different lengths of time. Get the children to work out from a given duration what the time was before a given time. Change the activity by giving them start and finish times so that the children work out how much time has passed.

Copymasters
C93 Time *Duration* The copymaster has 10 start times on it. Give the children the finish times and ask them to work out the length of time between the two. Answers are given for the following finish times: (1) 4:15, (2) 8:30, (3) 8:10, (4) 3:15, (5) 2:30, (6) 8:05, (7) 11:40, (8) 9:00, (9) 11:25, (10) 5:45. The copymaster can be reused with different finish times. You may wish to give the time taken and ask the children to work out the finish times.

C94 Time *Duration* The copymaster has two sets of times on it. Tell the children how much time to add to each set. Answers are given for: set A, half an hour; set B, quarter of an hour. This copymaster can be reused with various other times to add on. It can also be used for 'earlier than' exercises.

LEVEL 4/5

Learning Objectives

To be able to:
1. Convert to and from 12-hour and 24-hour time
2. Hours and minutes into minutes and vice versa
3. Use timetables
4. Add and subtract lengths of time
5. Work out the difference between times or duration

---

1 CONVERT TO AND FROM 12-HOUR AND 24-HOUR TIME
C95

Ideas for whole class work
Draw on the board a time line from midnight to midnight. Use colour to show am and pm. Plot a time in the am section and ask a child to plot what the time would be 12 hours later. Write next to it the time in 24-hour notation. Do this several times. Plot a time in the pm section and ask a child to plot what the time would be 12 hours earlier.

Copymasters
C95 Time *Convert time: 12-hour/24-hour* The copy-master has five blank clock faces and spaces for 12-hour and 24-hour time. Give the children the times which they then record in the three different ways. Answers are given for: (1) twenty past three in the morning; (2) quarter past one in the afternoon; (3) ten to five in the morning; (4) twenty-five to eight in the evening; (5) five past eleven in the evening.

2 HOURS AND MINUTES INTO MINUTES AND VICE VERSA
C96

Ideas for whole class work
The children work individually on the copymaster.

3	USE TIMETABLES
C97	

Ideas for whole class work

List four times on the board in a column, eg 11:45, 12:35, 13:00 and 13:30 and label them A, B, C and D. Tell the children to imagine it is part of a bus timetable and A, B, C and D are the various stops. Ask questions such as: what time does the bus leave C; what time does the bus arrive at D; how long does it take to get from A to B; if the bus is running 5 minutes late . . . Do this with other bus times. Remind the children to count up to whole hours first.

Copymasters
C97 Time *Use timetables*

4	ADD AND SUBTRACT LENGTHS OF TIME
C96	
C98	

Ideas for whole class work

1 *Add lengths of time* Adding time is only different from adding numbers when the sum goes over the hour boundary. Get the children to change minutes into hours and minutes and vice versa, eg 72 minutes: subtract 60 minutes (1 hour) and there are 12 minutes left which gives 1 hour and 12 minutes; 2 hours 20 minutes = 2 × 60 minutes + 20 minutes = 140 minutes.

2 *Add times* Write a time on the board, eg 2:15, and ask the children what the time would be after different lengths of time have passed. Start with whole, half and quarter hours, then ask what the time would be after 2 hours 25 minutes. Show the children that they just need to add the minutes as in normal addition but if the sum comes to

more than 60 they need to exchange the 60 minutes for 1 hour. For example, to work out 45 minutes later than 3:40, add 45 and 40 to make 85; 60 minutes of this is 1 hour so that 85 minutes is 1 hour 25 minutes which means the time will be 4:25. Some children find it easier to add on up to 60 first, then add on the rest.

Repeat the exercise using 24-hour time. Ask the children to work out lengths of time earlier than the given time as well.

Copymasters
C96 Time *Hours and minutes*

C98 Time *Add and subtract times* The copymaster has two sets of times on it. Give them a length of time to subtract from set A and to add to set B. Answers are given for: set A, 15 minutes earlier; set B, 25 minutes later.

5	WORK OUT THE DIFFERENCE BETWEEN TIMES OR DURATION
C99	
C100	

Ideas for whole class work

To cope with finding the difference between times, children need to be good at bonds to 60. Practise this with them using quick-fire numbers. You tell them a number and the children respond with the number that makes it up to 60. You could ask individual children in turn.

Move on to applying this to times. Start with one of the times as a whole hour. For example, from 08:35 to 10:00. First add from 08:35 to 09:00 which is 25 minutes, then add on the hour to 10:00. Writing it in steps can help some children to visualize what is happening. For example, ask how long it is from 07:15 to 10:20. From 07:15 to 08:00 to 10:00 to 10:20 is 45 minutes plus 2 hours plus 20 minutes which comes to 2 hours 65 minutes, so the answer is 3 hours 5 minutes.

Copymasters
C99 Time *Difference between times*

C100 Time *Time patterns*

Place Value
Round to the nearest 100

C2

Join each number to its nearest hundred

274

342

471

452

559

603

641

300

400

500

600

290

359

348

460

481

540

639

Place Value
Add 10 or 1

C1

1   479   →   ☐☐☐

2   582   →   ☐☐☐

3   320   →   ☐☐☐

4   649   →   ☐☐☐

5   219   →   ☐☐☐

6   721   →   ☐☐☐

7   769   →   ☐☐☐

8   590   →   ☐☐☐

9   831   →   ☐☐☐

10   159   →   ☐☐☐

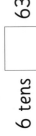

Name ___

Put in the correct sign: = , > or <

1 4 tens [ ] 43

2 23 [ ] 34

3 30 [ ] 3 tens

4 45 [ ] 54

5 90 [ ] 9 tens

6 39 [ ] 49

7 8 tens [ ] 8

8 12 [ ] 21

9 76 [ ] 67

10 10 tens [ ] 98

11 56 [ ] 6 tens

12 7 tens [ ] 47

13 81 [ ] 79

14 20 [ ] 2 tens

15 38 [ ] 4 tens

16 6 tens [ ] 63

17 27 [ ] 72

18 4 tens [ ] 40

19 51 [ ] 49

20 2 tens [ ] 19

Name ___

Less than 120	More than 120	Less than 210

More than 210	Less than 330	More than 330	Less than 550

More than 550	Less than 700	More than 700	Less than 910

26

Place Value
Multiply/divide by 10/100/1000 C5

Set A

1   760 → ☐
2   51 → ☐
3   410 → ☐
4   63 → ☐
5   1400 → ☐
6   32 → ☐
7   32000 → ☐
8   89 → ☐
9   81000 → ☐
10 924 → ☐

Place Value
Multiply by 10 C6

Match pairs where one number is
10 times the other

27   340

34   270   608

681   430   6810

123

151   1230   6080

501   43

1510   5010

Set B

1   34 → ☐
2   6·2 → ☐
3   436 → ☐
4   9·4 → ☐
5   130 → ☐
6   0·4 → ☐
7   560 → ☐
8   0·05 → ☐
9   57 → ☐
10 7·34 → ☐

27

Name

Fill in the missing operation and number

÷ or ×   10 or 100

1	43	□	=	430
2	39	□	=	3900
3	230	□	=	23
4	540	□	=	54
5	48	□	=	4800
6	720	□	=	7·2
7	40	□	=	400
8	7300	□	=	73
9	3600	□	=	36
10	17	□	=	1700

Name

Divide each number by 10

1	270 →	
2	4160 →	
3	374 →	
4	63 →	
5	340 →	
6	7390 →	
7	479 →	
8	82 →	

Multiply each number by 100

1	24 →	
2	39 →	
3	138 →	
4	921 →	
5	6 →	
6	41 →	
7	348 →	
8	7042 →	

Name _____

1 432 – [ ] = [ ]

2 526 – [ ] = [ ]

3 792 – [ ] = [ ]

4 851 – [ ] = [ ]

5 643 – [ ] = [ ]

6 1462 – [ ] = [ ]

7 7339 – [ ] = [ ]

8 9218 – [ ] = [ ]

9 74392 – [ ] = [ ]

10 62134 – [ ] = [ ]

Name _____

What is the:

1 smallest three-digit number

2 largest three-digit number

3 smallest three-digit number with no repeated digits

4 largest three-digit number with no repeated digits

5 smallest four-digit number without using 0

6 largest four-digit number

7 smallest four-digit number with no repeated digits

8 smallest five-digit number without using 0

9 largest five-digit number with no repeated digits

10 smallest five-digit number with no repeated digits

29

Name _____

Ring the sums that make 20

17 + 3	14 + 6	7 + 12
19 + 1	4 + 16	
20 + 0	13 + 8	10 + 10
11 + 7	8 + 12	3 + 16
2 + 18	9 + 12	
13 + 7	9 + 11	0 + 19
1 + 19	16 + 4	
5 + 16	10 + 10	12 + 8
11 + 9	18 + 3	
7 + 13	15 + 5	

30

Name _____

Ring two numbers that add up to 100 in each box

27	37	47	52	36	46
	83	73		54	63
48	38	52	17	26	94
	12	58		14	74
72	74	36	49	51	59
	18	28		44	31
68	58	32	14	16	76
	85	52		84	74
23	17	77	59	49	39
	63	67		61	41
36	46	43	88	92	22
	66	64		12	18

1	20	40	60
2	30	50	70
3	40	60	80
4	30	50	70
5	20	40	60
6	50	70	90
7	60	80	100
8	20	40	60
9	50	70	90
10	60	80	100

Set A

1 27 → ☐
2 41 → ☐
3 68 → ☐
4 19 → ☐
5 6 → ☐
6 52 → ☐
7 75 → ☐
8 14 → ☐
9 32 → ☐
10 26 → ☐

Set B

1 48 → ☐
2 33 → ☐
3 12 → ☐
4 29 → ☐
5 55 → ☐
6 64 → ☐
7 42 → ☐
8 21 → ☐
9 59 → ☐
10 17 → ☐

31

Name _____

Set A

1   43 →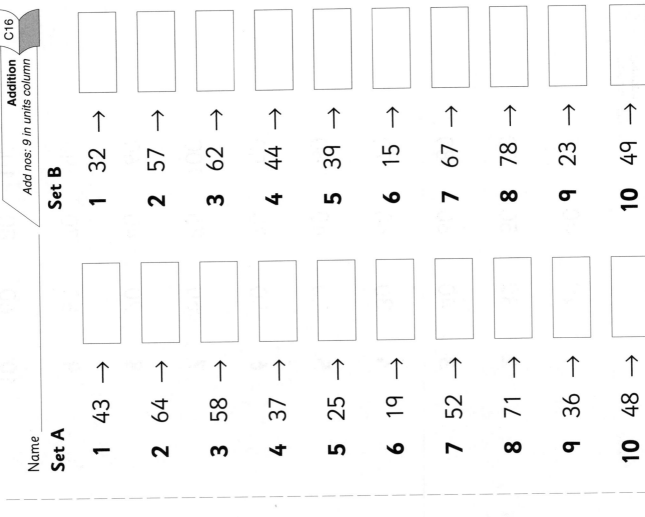
2   64 →
3   58 →
4   37 →
5   25 →
6   19 →
7   52 →
8   71 →
9   36 →
10   48 →

Set B

1   32 →
2   57 →
3   62 →
4   44 →
5   39 →
6   15 →
7   67 →
8   78 →
9   23 →
10   49 →

Name _____

Pick 3 numbers from the box and add them.
Do this 4 times to make 4 different totals.

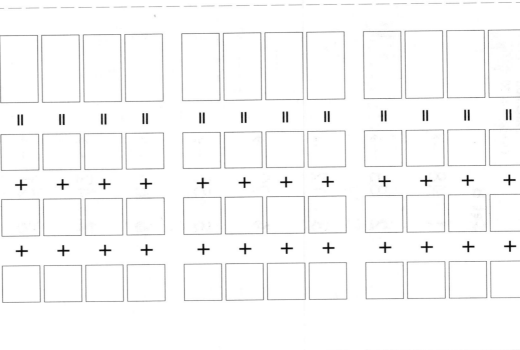

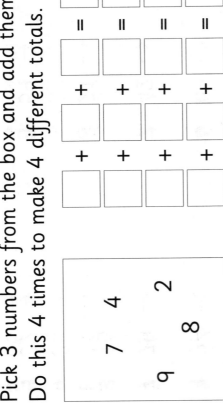

7   4
9   2
8

6   7
5   9
3

8   3
5   7
1

Name _____

	Add units	Add tens	Total
eg 27 + 34	7 + 4 = 11	20 + 30 = 50	11 + 50 = 61
1 42 + 53			
2 56 + 28			
3 39 + 52			
4 64 + 26			
5 35 + 26			
6 17 + 46			
7 52 + 48			
8 33 + 48			
9 37 + 39			
10 41 + 28			

Name _____

Set A

1 23 →
2 53 →
3 43 →
4 83 →
5 13 →
6 63 →

Set B

1 57 →
2 27 →
3 77 →
4 67 →
5 47 →
6 17 →

Set C

1 76 →
2 46 →
3 16 →
4 36 →
5 66 →
6 26 →

Set D

1 39 →
2 79 →
3 49 →
4 69 →
5 19 →
6 59 →

33

Name _____

Approximate to the nearest 10, then add.

eg
```
  27      30
+ 48      50
        ────
          80
```

1
```
  32      □  □
+ 59      ── □
```

2
```
  47      □  □
+ 33      ── □
```

3
```
  44      □  □
+ 31      ── □
```

4
```
  29      □  □
+ 57      ── □
```

Approximate to the nearest 100, then add.

5
```
  131      □  □
+ 486      ── □
```

6
```
  381      □  □
+ 529      ── □
```

7
```
  362      □  □
+ 294      ── □
```

8
```
  444      □  □
+ 378      ── □
```

Name _____

Make one number into a whole number of tens, then work out the answer.

eg 58 + 33 → 60 + 31 [   ]

1   39 + 46 → 40 + 45 [   ]

2   28 + 37 → 30 + 35 [   ]

3   46 + 25 → 50 + □ [   ]

4   37 + 26 → □ + □ [   ]

5   49 + 46 → □ + □ [   ]

6   26 + 29 → □ + □ [   ]

7   38 + 47 → □ + □ [   ]

8   57 + 35 → □ + □ [   ]

9   68 + 27 → □ + □ [   ]

10 48 + 35 → □ + □ [   ]

34

Name ___

Make the number up to the next whole ten

1	26 to 30	add on	☐
2	41 to 50	add on	☐
3	37 to 40	add on	☐
4	72 to ☐	add on	☐
5	53 to ☐	add on	☐
6	88 to ☐	add on	☐
7	64 to ☐	add on	☐
8	79 to ☐	add on	☐
9	56 to ☐	add on	☐
10	65 to ☐	add on	☐

Set A

1 19 → ☐
2 12 → ☐
3 17 → ☐
4 15 → ☐
5 18 → ☐

Set B

1 20 → ☐
2 13 → ☐
3 18 → ☐
4 11 → ☐
5 16 → ☐

Set C

1 14 → ☐
2 19 → ☐
3 16 → ☐
4 20 → ☐
5 13 → ☐

Set D

1 17 → ☐
2 11 → ☐
3 15 → ☐
4 18 → ☐
5 20 → ☐

35

Set B

Number given

1 40 →

2 52 →

3 37 →

4 26 →

5 71 →

6 65 →

7 48 →

8 33 →

9 69 →

10 44 →

Set A

Number given

1 20 →

2 41 →

3 54 →

4 32 →

5 64 →

6 29 →

7 38 →

8 46 →

9 25 →

10 57 →

Work these out in your head

1 100 marbles, lose 27. How many left? ☐

2 100 grapes, 42 rot. How many left? ☐

3 100 seeds, 36 die. How many grow? ☐

4 100 flies, 61 fly away. How many left? ☐

5 100 hares, 73 run away. How many left? ☐

What is the difference between the numbers?

6 31, 56   difference = ☐

7 92, 48   difference = ☐

8 83, 34   difference = ☐

9 64, 29   difference = ☐

10 75, 47   difference = ☐

Name _____

Circle any five numbers in each set

Set A

24   34   42

44   28

38   48   32

Set B

53   57   73

65   55

67   63   77

Set C

31   49   59   46

51   36

41   39

Set A

Start number

1   – 3 – 2 – 7 = ☐

2   – 4 – 1 – 2 = ☐

3   – 6 – 2 – 3 = ☐

4   – 8 – 1 – 4 = ☐

5   – 5 – 2 – 3 = ☐

6   – 3 – 6 – 4 = ☐

7   – 7 – 2 – 3 = ☐

8   – 9 – 2 – 2 = ☐

9   – 5 – 7 – 2 = ☐

10 – 4 – 7 – 1 = ☐

Set B

Start number

1   – 5 – 7 – 2 = ☐

2   – 3 – 8 – 3 = ☐

3   – 9 – 2 – 4 = ☐

4   –12 – 2 – 3 = ☐

5   –11 – 5 – 3 = ☐

6   – 8 – 7 – 4 = ☐

7   – 3 – 4 – 5 = ☐

8   – 4 – 7 – 2 = ☐

9   – 8 – 3 – 4 = ☐

10 – 5 – 6 – 3 = ☐

Name ___

Change the numbers so that one of them is a whole number of tens, then subtract

1 27 – 19 = 28 – 20 = ☐

2 48 – 29 = 49 – 30 = ☐

3 64 – 39 = 65 – ☐ = ☐

4 73 – 49 = 74 – ☐ = ☐

5 56 – 29 = 57 – ☐ = ☐

6 47 – 19 = ☐ – ☐ = ☐

7 65 – 29 = ☐ – ☐ = ☐

8 74 – 39 = ☐ – ☐ = ☐

9 92 – 59 = ☐ – ☐ = ☐

10 81 – 49 = ☐ – ☐ = ☐

Name ___

Ring the sums with an answer of 16

27 – 11   45 – 19

52 – 38   71 – 55

          62 – 44

39 – 23   48 – 31

50 – 33   45 – 29   64 – 48

84 – 58   53 – 37

97 – 81   91 – 75

Name

Solve these problems

1 Anita has 73 stamps. John has 18 fewer.

How many has John? ☐

2 The difference between Sarah's and her mother's ages is 29 years. Her mother is 43.

How old is Sarah? ☐

3 Alan scored 27 runs. Ben scored 73.

What is the difference? ☐

4 Rob gets 83 marks in his test. Jack gets 68.

What is the difference between their marks? ☐

5 From Redridge to Fordwell is 97 km. If I travel 39 km, how much further is it? ☐

6 Annie has 56 slabs to lay for a patio. She lays 27.

How many has she left to do? ☐

Name

Use addition to check these subtraction sums

1 $37 - 18 = 19$ → $19 + 18 =$ ☐

2 $46 - 19 =$ ☐ → ☐ $+ 19 =$ ☐

3 $58 - 26 =$ ☐ → ☐ $+ 26 =$ ☐

4 $72 - 34 =$ ☐ → ☐ $+ 34 =$ ☐

5 $83 - 55 =$ ☐ → ☐ $+ 55 =$ ☐

Use subtraction to check these addition sums

6 $23 + 34 = 57$ → $57 - 34 =$ ☐

7 $35 + 47 =$ ☐ → ☐ $- 47 = 35$

8 $18 + 24 =$ ☐ → ☐ $- 24 =$ ☐

9 $26 + 17 =$ ☐ → ☐ $- 17 =$ ☐

10 $53 + 29 =$ ☐ → ☐ $- 29 =$ ☐

39

Name _____

Set A

| 12 | 5 | 35 | 15 |
| 4 | 9 | 20 | 10 |

Set B

| 5 | 9 | 50 | 20 |
| 8 | 15 | 6 | 16 |

Set C

10	18	90
15	25
4	70	12

Set D

20	15
4	12	10
6	9	16

Name _____

Set A   × ☐

1. 4 → ☐
2. 6 → ☐
3. 9 → ☐
4. 3 → ☐
5. 7 → ☐

Set B   × ☐

1. 2 → ☐
2. 10 → ☐
3. 4 → ☐
4. 8 → ☐
5. 5 → ☐

Set C   × ☐

1. 10 → ☐
2. 8 → ☐
3. 5 → ☐
4. 3 → ☐
5. 6 → ☐

Set D   × ☐

1. 10 → ☐
2. 4 → ☐
3. 2 → ☐
4. 7 → ☐
5. 9 → ☐

Name

1 3 children have 4 sweets each.

[ ] sweets altogether.

2 5 chairs, 4 legs each.

[ ] legs altogether.

3 7 coats, 5 buttons each.

[ ] buttons altogether.

4 8 rabbits, 2 ears each.

[ ] ears altogether.

5 5 lines of chairs, 12 chairs in each line.

[ ] chairs altogether.

6 10 lines of lettuces, 10 lettuces in each line.

[ ] lettuces altogether.

7 6 bunches of flowers, 5 flowers in each bunch.

[ ] flowers altogether.

8 4 children, 2 books each.

[ ] books altogether.

9 10 cars, 4 wheels each.

[ ] wheels altogether.

10 6 twigs, 10 leaves on each.

[ ] leaves altogether.

Name

	× 2	× 5	× 10
1			
5			
8			
11			
3			
12			
6			
0			
10			
7			
2			
4			
9			

Time: _____

Name

Set A

	×	☐
1	4	→
2	9	→
3	6	→
4	8	→

☐ ☐ ☐ ☐

Set B

	×	☐
1	5	→
2	10	→
3	7	→
4	3	→

☐ ☐ ☐ ☐

Set C

	×	☐
1	2	→
2	9	→
3	7	→
4	5	→

☐ ☐ ☐ ☐

Set D

	×	☐
1	6	→
2	8	→
3	3	→
4	10	→

☐ ☐ ☐ ☐

Name

	× ☐	× ☐	× ☐
3			
6			
10			
4			
1			
7			
9			
5			
2			
8			

Time: _____

Name

Fill in the missing number

1. $4 \times \square = 32$

2. $\square \times 7 = 42$

3. $6 \times 9 = \square$

4. $5 \times \square = 50$

5. $\square \times 8 = 64$

6. $3 \times 7 = \square$

7. $9 \times \square = 81$

8. $\square \times 8 = 56$

9. $10 \times 10 = \square$

10. $7 \times \square = 49$

Name

Ring the numbers which should **not** be in the set

four times table

48   36   34   36

12   26

six times table

48   36   32   42

52   24

eight times table

34   54

16   28   54   64

80

three times table

32

49   18   30

21   25

nine times table

56   34   63

27   35

78   81   54   21

seven times table

32

49   35   63

54   21

Name _____

Set A

1 3 × 4 = □

2 3 × 40 = □

3 30 × 40 = □

4 30 × 4 = □

5 5 × 7 = □

6 5 × 70 = □

7 50 × 70 = □

8 50 × 7 = □

Set B

1 20 × 8 = □

2 50 × 6 = □

3 40 × 9 = □

4 8 × 70 = □

5 30 × 7 = □

6 60 × 60 = □

7 40 × 80 = □

8 30 × 90 = □

9 50 × 50 = □

10 70 × 60 = □

Name _____

Complete the sets

Set A

6 × 8 = □

8 × 6 = □

□ ÷ 6 = 8

□ ÷ 8 = 6

Set B

9 × 4 = □

4 × 9 = □

□ ÷ 4 = 9

□ ÷ 9 = 4

Set C

8 × 7 = □

□ × 7 = □

□ ÷ □ = □

□ ÷ □ = □

Set D

7 × 6 = □

□ × □ = □

□ ÷ □ = □

□ ÷ □ = □

Can be divided
by 5

Can be divided
by 2

Can be divided
by 10

Can be divided
by 5

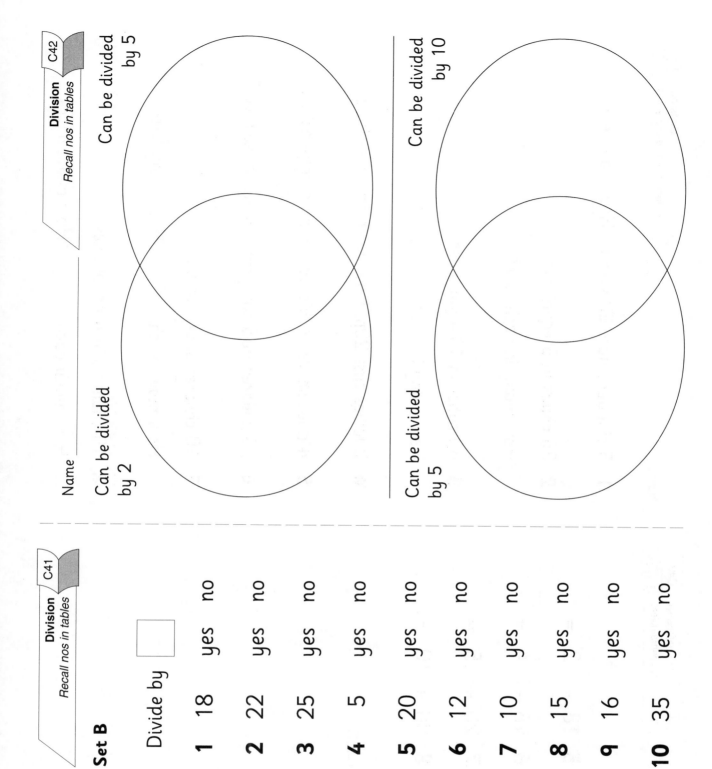

Name ____

Set A

Divide by [ ]

1	14	yes	no
2	33	yes	no
3	45	yes	no
4	15	yes	no
5	10	yes	no
6	4	yes	no
7	16	yes	no
8	20	yes	no
9	25	yes	no
10	35	yes	no

Set B

Divide by [ ]

1	18	yes	no
2	22	yes	no
3	25	yes	no
4	5	yes	no
5	20	yes	no
6	12	yes	no
7	10	yes	no
8	15	yes	no
9	16	yes	no
10	35	yes	no

1 5 children share 20 sweets. How many each? ☐

2 25 chairs in 5 equal rows.

How many in each row? ☐

3 60 cubes in 10 equal piles.

How many in each pile? ☐

4 2 lollies cost 20p. How much each are they? ☐

5 4 dogs share 16 biscuits. How many each? ☐

6 15 children in 5 cars. How many in each car? ☐

7 10 children share 33 biscuits.

How many each? ☐   How many left? ☐

8 19 counters in 4 equal piles.

How many each? ☐   How many left? ☐

Work out these answers

1 $20 \div 2 =$ ☐

2 $15 \div 5 =$ ☐

3 $40 \div 10 =$ ☐

4 $35 \div 5 =$ ☐

5 $18 \div 2 =$ ☐

6 $16 \div 4 =$ ☐

7 $20 \div 5 =$ ☐

8 $80 \div 10 =$ ☐

Some of these have remainders

9 $19 \div 2 =$ ☐ r ☐

10 $45 \div 5 =$ ☐ r ☐

11 $10 \div 3 =$ ☐ r ☐

12 $13 \div 4 =$ ☐ r ☐

13 $17 \div 2 =$ ☐ r ☐

14 $28 \div 5 =$ ☐ r ☐

46

Set B

Divisible by ☐

36

48   40

42   32

56

54   72

Set A

Name _____

Divisible by ☐

56

42

49   48

36

54

42   25

36   19

31   18

43   10

Set D

Divisible by ☐

81

72   80

64

54   45

48

Set C

Divisible by ☐

28

45   54

56

36   63

26   37

49   50

13   41

34   55

Name _____

Set A

1 $27 \div 3 =$ ☐

2 $270 \div 3 =$ ☐

3 $2700 \div 3 =$ ☐

4 $2700 \div 30 =$ ☐

5 $54 \div 9 =$ ☐

6 $540 \div 9 =$ ☐

7 $5400 \div 9 =$ ☐

8 $5400 \div 90 =$ ☐

Set B

1 $450 \div 9 =$ ☐

2 $720 \div 8 =$ ☐

3 $3600 \div 6 =$ ☐

4 $4800 \div 8 =$ ☐

5 $320 \div 4 =$ ☐

6 $3200 \div 80 =$ ☐

7 $8100 \div 90 =$ ☐

8 $5600 \div 80 =$ ☐

9 $420 \div 60 =$ ☐

10 $6300 \div 90 =$ ☐

Name _____

Put the numbers in the correct boxes

3, 5, 6, 8, 15, 16, 24, 32, 33, 34

	divisible by 3	not divisible by 3
divisible by 8		
not divisible by 8		

12, 18, 21, 24, 31, 36, 45, 48, 63, 64

	divisible by 6	not divisible by 6
divisible by 9		
not divisible by 9		

Work out the answers as quickly as you can

1 24 ÷ 3 = ☐

2 36 ÷ 9 = ☐

3 42 ÷ 6 = ☐

4 21 ÷ 7 = ☐

5 35 ÷ 5 = ☐

6 60 ÷ 10 = ☐

7 18 ÷ 2 = ☐

8 54 ÷ 9 = ☐

9 32 ÷ 4 = ☐

10 40 ÷ 8 = ☐

11 64 ÷ 8 = ☐

12 36 ÷ 6 = ☐

13 24 ÷ 4 = ☐

14 63 ÷ 9 = ☐

15 16 ÷ 2 = ☐

16 45 ÷ 5 = ☐

17 80 ÷ 10 = ☐

18 49 ÷ 7 = ☐

19 18 ÷ 6 = ☐

20 27 ÷ 3 = ☐

Solve the problems. Check by multiplying.

1 56 chairs in 8 equal rows.

☐ chairs in each row.

☐ × 8 = ☐

2 81 bulbs planted in 9 equal rows.

☐ bulbs in each row.

☐ × 9 = ☐

3 49 children in 7 teams.

☐ in each team.

☐ × ☐ = ☐

4 72 biscuits in 8 packets.

☐ biscuits in each.

☐ × ☐ = ☐

5 How many dogs have a total of 36 legs?

☐ dogs.

☐ × ☐ = ☐

6 42 eggs are used to make 7 cakes. How many for each cake?

☐ × ☐ = ☐

49

Number Patterns
Doubling and halving

Name

Tick the box if one number is double the other

1 14, 7   ☐
2 3, 8   ☐
3 5, 10   ☐
4 8, 4   ☐
5 13, 24   ☐
6 4, 2   ☐
7 7, 4   ☐
8 12, 5   ☐
9 8, 16   ☐
10 20, 10   ☐
11 12, 26   ☐
12 6, 3   ☐
13 11, 22   ☐
14 19, 9   ☐
15 12, 6   ☐
16 9, 18   ☐

Number Patterns
Recognize/continue patterns

Name

Spot the pattern. What comes next?

1 2, 4, 6, 8   ☐ ☐   Pattern +2
2 1, 4, 7, 10   ☐ ☐   Pattern ☐
3 17, 15, 13, 11   ☐ ☐   Pattern −
4 18, 15, 12, 9   ☐ ☐   Pattern ☐
5 3, 5, 7, 9   ☐ ☐   Pattern ☐
6 2, 5, 8, 11   ☐ ☐   Pattern ☐
7 22, 19, 16, 13   ☐ ☐   Pattern ☐
8 1, 5, 9, 13   ☐ ☐   Pattern ☐

Number Patterns
Inverse operations

1	5	5
2	7	7
3	10	10
4	6	6
5	8	8
6	12	12
7	9	9
8	4	4
9	11	11
10	15	15

Number Patterns
Input-output machines

Set A

IN		OUT
7		
10		
3		
8		

Set B

IN		OUT
4		
6		
11		
9		

Set C

IN		OUT
12		
9		
14		
10		

Set D

IN		OUT
13		
8		
11		
15		

Name _____

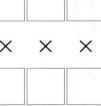
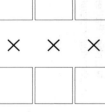
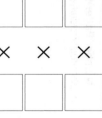
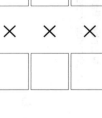

1   6   6

2   3   3

3   7   7

4   5   5

5   8   8

Name _____

List the factors in pairs

<u>18</u>
1 × ☐ ☐ ☐
2 × ☐ ☐ ☐
× ☐

<u>32</u>
1 × ☐ ☐ ☐
× ☐ ☐

<u>40</u>
1 × ☐ ☐ ☐ ☐
× ☐ ☐ ☐

<u>12</u>
1 × 12
2 × ☐ ☐
× ☐

<u>20</u>
1 × ☐ ☐ ☐
× ☐ ☐

<u>24</u>
1 × ☐ ☐ ☐ ☐
× ☐ ☐ ☐

Name _____

What comes next? Describe the pattern.

1 1, 4, 9, 16, ☐ ☐

Pattern _____

2 1, 2, 4, 7, ☐ ☐

Pattern _____

3 64, 32, 16, 8, ☐ ☐

Pattern _____

4 1, 3, 7, 15, ☐ ☐

Pattern _____

5 1, 4, 10, 19, ☐ ☐

Pattern _____

Name _____

Continue the pattern. What is the rule?

IN	OUT
1	5
2	6
3	7
4	☐

IN	OUT
1	2
2	4
3	6
4	☐

IN	OUT
1	3
2	5
3	7
4	☐

IN	OUT
1	2
2	5
3	8
4	☐

Name _____

What is the number?

1 I think of a number, double it and add 1.

The answer is 9. What is the number? ☐

2 I think of a number, subtract 2 and double it.

The answer is 10. What is the number? ☐

3 I think of a number, add 4 and divide by 3.

The answer is 4. What is the number? ☐

4 I think of a number, divide by 2 and add 3.

The answer is 7. What is the number? ☐

5 I think of a number, add 3, multiply by 2 and subtract 5. The answer is 13.

What is the number? ☐

Name _____

Set A

4
6
3
7

Set B

5
2
8
4

Set C

8
3
6

Set D

5
9
6

Name ___

What fraction is shaded? Fill in the gaps.

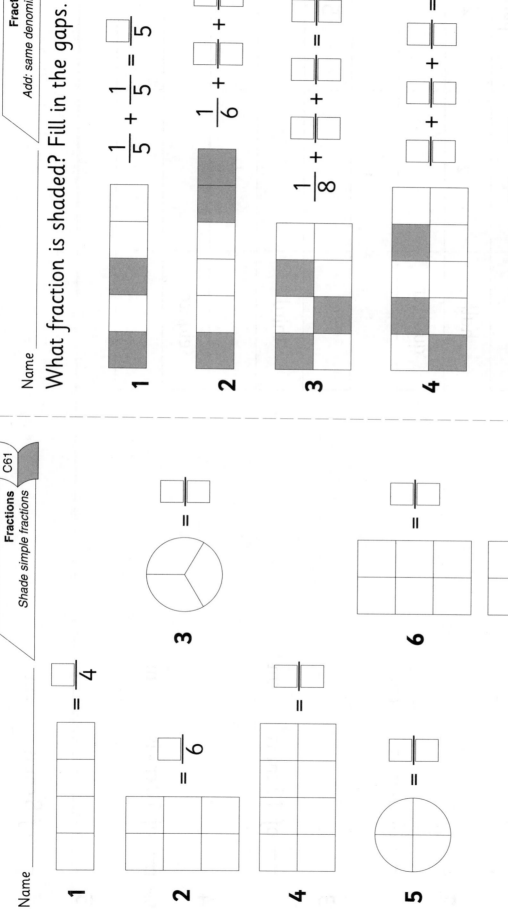

1. $\dfrac{1}{5} + \dfrac{1}{5} = \dfrac{\square}{5}$

2. $\dfrac{1}{6} + \dfrac{\square}{\square} + \dfrac{\square}{\square} = \dfrac{\square}{\square}$

3. $\dfrac{1}{8} + \dfrac{\square}{\square} = \dfrac{\square}{\square}$

4. $\dfrac{\square}{\square} + \dfrac{\square}{\square} + \dfrac{\square}{\square} = \dfrac{\square}{\square}$

5. $\dfrac{\square}{\square} + \dfrac{\square}{\square} + \dfrac{\square}{\square} = \dfrac{\square}{\square}$

6. $\dfrac{\square}{\square} + \dfrac{\square}{\square} = \dfrac{\square}{\square}$

Name ___

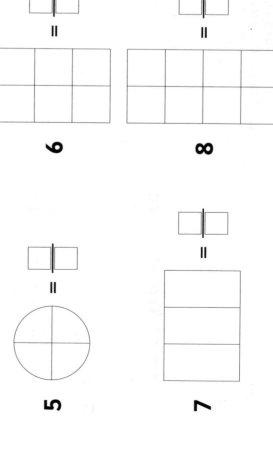

1. $= \dfrac{\square}{4}$

2. $= \dfrac{\square}{6}$

3. $= \dfrac{\square}{\square}$

4. $= \dfrac{\square}{\square}$

5. $= \dfrac{\square}{\square}$

6. $= \dfrac{\square}{\square}$

7. $= \dfrac{\square}{\square}$

8. $= \dfrac{\square}{\square}$

Name _____

Fill in the gaps

In words	Fraction	How many equal parts
half	$\frac{1}{2}$	2
quarter		
	$\frac{1}{10}$	
		5
third		
	$\frac{1}{6}$	
eighth		
		9

Name _____

1 ⬚/⬚ of 4 cm is [ ] cm

2 ⬚/⬚ of 6 cm is [ ] cm

3 ⬚/⬚ of 12 cm is [ ] cm

4 ⬚/⬚ of 10 cm is [ ] cm

5 ⬚/⬚ of 8 cm is [ ] cm

Name

Find the number

1 $\frac{1}{2}$ of a number is 7.　　The number is ▢

2 $\frac{1}{4}$ of a number is 6.　　The number is ▢

3 $\frac{1}{5}$ of a number is 5.　　The number is ▢

4 $\frac{1}{3}$ of a number is 7.　　The number is ▢

5 $\frac{1}{10}$ of a number is 4.　　The number is ▢

6 $\frac{2}{3}$ of a number is 6.　　The number is ▢

7 $\frac{2}{5}$ of a number is 8.　　The number is ▢

8 $\frac{3}{10}$ of a number is 15.　　The number is ▢

Name

Find the number

1 $\frac{1}{4}$ of 20 = ▢

2 $\frac{1}{3}$ of 15 = ▢

3 $\frac{1}{5}$ of 20 = ▢

4 $\frac{1}{4}$ of 16 = ▢

5 $\frac{1}{10}$ of 20 = ▢

6 $\frac{1}{5}$ of 30 = ▢

7 $\frac{1}{3}$ of 18 = ▢

8 $\frac{1}{4}$ of 40 = ▢

9 $\frac{2}{5}$ of 15 = ▢

10 $\frac{2}{3}$ of 12 = ▢

11 $\frac{3}{4}$ of 24 = ▢

12 $\frac{3}{5}$ of 25 = ▢

13 $\frac{7}{10}$ of 30 = ▢

14 $\frac{4}{5}$ of 50 = ▢

15 $\frac{3}{10}$ of 80 = ▢

16 $\frac{9}{10}$ of 70 = ▢

$\dfrac{1}{2}$

$\dfrac{1}{4}$

$\dfrac{1}{3}$

$\dfrac{1}{5}$

Put in the correct sign: < or >

Set A

$\dfrac{1}{2}$

$\dfrac{2}{5}$

$\dfrac{1}{4}$

$\dfrac{3}{10}$

Set B

$\dfrac{2}{5}$

$\dfrac{2}{3}$

$\dfrac{1}{2}$

$\dfrac{3}{4}$

Set C

$\dfrac{3}{5}$

$\dfrac{1}{2}$

$\dfrac{3}{4}$

$\dfrac{5}{8}$

Set D

$\dfrac{2}{3}$

$\dfrac{2}{6}$

$\dfrac{2}{5}$

$\dfrac{3}{10}$

Name _____

1 How many seconds in one-fifth of a minute? □

2 How many hours in one-sixth of a day? □

3 How many mm in one-fifth of a cm? □

4 How many days in two-sevenths of a fortnight? □

5 How many cm in three-tenths of a metre? □

6 How many minutes in one-third of an hour? □

7 How many hours in one-quarter of a day? □

8 How many cm in two-fifths of a metre? □

Name _____

Shade to show equivalent fractions

1 $\dfrac{1}{2} = \dfrac{\Box}{\Box}$

2 $\dfrac{1}{4} = \dfrac{\Box}{\Box}$

3 $\dfrac{1}{10} = \dfrac{\Box}{\Box}$

4 $\dfrac{1}{3} = \dfrac{\Box}{\Box}$

5 $\dfrac{1}{5} = \dfrac{\Box}{\Box}$

6 $\dfrac{2}{3} = \dfrac{\Box}{\Box}$

Round off the numbers to the nearest whole number.

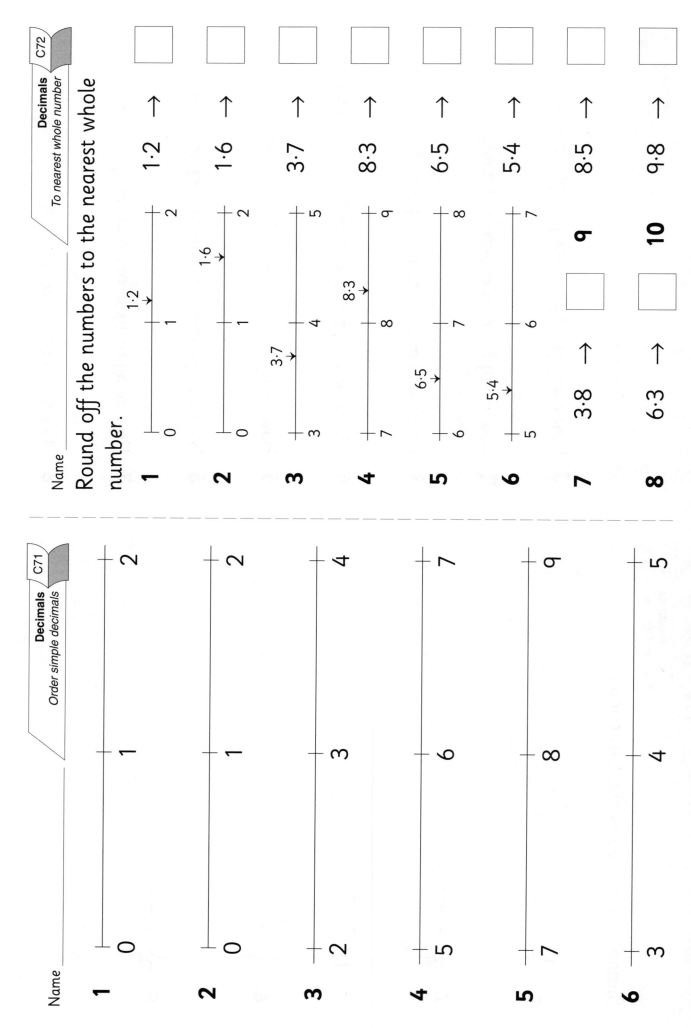

1. 1·2 → ☐
2. 1·6 → ☐
3. 3·7 → ☐
4. 8·3 → ☐
5. 6·5 → ☐
6. 5·4 → ☐
7. 3·8 → ☐
8. 6·3 → ☐
9. 8·5 → ☐
10. 9·8 → ☐

---

1. 0 — 1 — 2
2. 0 — 1 — 2
3. 2 — 3 — 4
4. 5 — 6 — 7
5. 7 — 8 — 9
6. 3 — 4 — 5

Name

Set A

1 2·2 → ☐
2 4·6 → ☐
3 5·8 → ☐
4 1·4 → ☐
5 3·5 → ☐
6 7·9 → ☐
7 4·0 → ☐
8 8·1 → ☐
9 2·9 → ☐
10 9·9 → ☐

Set B

1 4·2 → ☐
2 5·6 → ☐
3 3·7 → ☐
4 2·8 → ☐
5 8·3 → ☐
6 5·9 → ☐
7 3·9 → ☐
8 2·0 → ☐
9 8·9 → ☐
10 1·0 → ☐

Name

Join pairs of numbers that add to make 8

2·6   3·3

3·5   4·5

1·8   5·4

6·2   2·5

5·5   4·7

2·3

Join pairs with a difference of 0·4

2·2   3·4

1·9   3·8

2·6   6·2

5·8   4·5

4·9

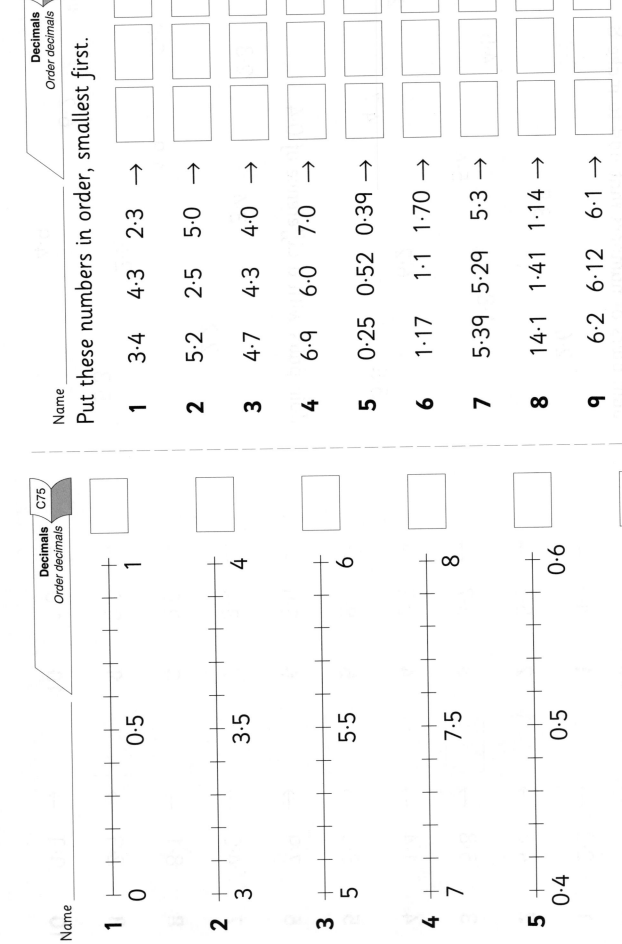

Name _____

Put these numbers in order, smallest first.

1   3·4   4·3   2·3   →

2   5·2   2·5   5·0   →

3   4·7   4·3   4·0   →

4   6·9   6·0   7·0   →

5   0·25   0·52   0·39   →

6   1·17   1·1   1·70   →

7   5·39   5·29   5·3   →

8   14·1   1·41   1·14   →

9   6·2   6·12   6·1   →

10   7·51   7·5   7·49   →

Name _____

1   0   0·5   1

2   3   3·5   4

3   5   5·5   6

4   7   7·5   8

5   0·4   0·5   0·6

6   1·5   1·6   1·7

Multiply/divide: 10, 100, 1000

Name ___

Ring the correct answer

1	$27 \div 10 =$	270	**6**	$3.43 \times 10 =$	343
		2.7			34.3
		0.27			3.043

1 $27 \div 10 =$ 270 2.7 0.27

6 $3.43 \times 10 =$ 343 34.3 3.043

2 $4.2 \times 100 =$ 42 4.20 420

7 $26.2 \times 100 =$ 262.0 2.62 2620

3 $3.6 \times 1000 =$ 360 3600 36.00

8 $9 \div 100 =$ 9.00 0.9 0.09

4 $51.3 \div 10 =$ 51.30 0.513 5.13

9 $5.7 \times 100 =$ 570 57 5700

5 $17 \div 100 =$ 0.17 1.7 1.07

10 $83 \div 100 =$ 0.83 8.30 8.03

Add and subtract decimals

Name ___

1 3·4

2 7·6

3 8·1

4 6·3

5 2·5

6 5·7

7 6·8

8 4·31

9 5·24

10 3·12

Name _____

Put a square round numbers with five-tenths.
Put a ring round numbers with five-hundredths.

3·52   5·64   4·35

4·5   2·45

9·15   8·52   1·51

3·05   7·51   5·62

5·39   6·35

Name _____

1 What is eight thousand divided by

a hundred? ☐

2 What is fourteen point two multiplied

by ten? ☐

3 What number is five more than 3·6? ☐

4 How many more is two point five three than

one point four three? ☐

5 What number is one tenth more than

seven point nine? ☐

6 Half a number is three point four.

What is the number? ☐

Change to pounds

1 400p = £ _____

2 350p = £ _____

3 560p = £ _____

4 824p = £ _____

5 720p = £ _____

6 603p = £ _____

7 94p = £ _____

8 50p = £ _____

9 6p = £ _____

10 12p = £ _____

Change to pence

11 £5.25 = _____ p

12 £7.30 = _____ p

13 £1.26 = _____ p

14 £3.40 = _____ p

15 £4.07 = _____ p

16 £3 = _____ p

17 £0.28 = _____ p

18 £0.07 = _____ p

19 £0.60 = _____ p

20 £6 = _____ p

---

1 _____ p is _____ 5 pences and _____ 2 pences

2 _____ p is _____ 5 pences and _____ 2 pences

3 _____ p is _____ 5 pences and _____ 2 pences

4 _____ p is _____ 5 pences and _____ 2 pences

5 _____ p is _____ 5 pences and _____ 2 pences

6 _____ p is _____ 10 pences and _____ 5 pences

_____ 2 pences and _____ 1 pences

7 _____ p is _____ 10 pences and _____ 5 pences

_____ 2 pences and _____ 1 pences

8 _____ p is _____ 10 pences and _____ 5 pences

_____ 2 pences and _____ 1 pences

Name _____

How much change from £1

1 Spend 64p. Change [ ] p

2 Spend 29p. Change [ ] p

3 Buy two lollies for 24p each.
   Spend [ ] p. Change [ ] p

4 Buy three peaches for 30p each.
   Spend [ ] p. Change [ ] p

5 Buy five chews for 7p each.
   Spend [ ] p. Change [ ] p

How much change from £5

6 Spend £4.50. Change [ ]

7 Spend £3.20. Change [ ]

8 Spend £2.80. Change [ ]

Name _____

Set A

add [ ] p

1 £1.20 → £ [ ]

2 £3.40 → £ [ ]

3 £6.80 → £ [ ]

4 £7.90 → £ [ ]

5 £4.63 → £ [ ]

6 £8.92 → £ [ ]

7 £5.98 → £ [ ]

8 £1.04 → £ [ ]

9 £6.08 → £ [ ]

10 £0.99 → £ [ ]

Set B

subtract [ ] p

1 £4.50 → £ [ ]

2 £6.70 → £ [ ]

3 £3.90 → £ [ ]

4 £5.10 → £ [ ]

5 £7.23 → £ [ ]

6 £8.14 → £ [ ]

7 £9.03 → £ [ ]

8 £2.08 → £ [ ]

9 £0.64 → £ [ ]

10 £1.01 → £ [ ]

66

Name _____

Set A

add

1 £1.30 →
2 £3.10 →
3 £5.98 →
4 £6.04 →
5 £8.83 →
6 £12.18 →
7 £15.92 →
8 £17.88 →
9 £3.99 →
10 £7.94 →

Set B

subtract

1 £2.40 →
2 £7.30 →
3 £4.61 →
4 £3.17 →
5 £12.94 →
6 £5.07 →
7 £8.13 →
8 £4.02 →
9 £9.12 →
10 £15.21 →

Name _____

Set A

Make up to £ ☐

1 £2.20 →
2 £6.15 →
3 £3.45 →
4 £1.95 →
5 £2.06 →
6 £4.17 →
7 £5.81 →
8 £6.04 →
9 £1.12 →
10 £4.63 →

Set B

Make up to £ ☐

1 £3.50 →
2 £4.25 →
3 £1.75 →
4 £5.45 →
5 £2.61 →
6 £4.26 →
7 £5.39 →
8 £3.72 →
9 £1.83 →
10 £4.44 →

Name _____

Find the total cost

1 4 books at £2.99 each   £ [ ]

2 6 tapes at £6.99 each   £ [ ]

3 3 shirts at £4.99 each   £ [ ]

4 7 balls at £1.98 each   £ [ ]

5 5 pens at £3.98 each   £ [ ]

6 £1.99 + £4.99 =   £ [ ]

7 £3.99 + £6.99 =   £ [ ]

8 £2.98 + £5.99 =   £ [ ]

9 £7.98 + £4.98 =   £ [ ]

10 £6.99 + £1.99 + £3.98 =   £ [ ]

Name _____

If Alan saves 50p a week, how many weeks will it be before he can buy:

1 a book for £4.99?   [ ] weeks

2 a pen for £3.42?   [ ] weeks

3 a cap for £6.19?   [ ] weeks

4 a football for £8.75?   [ ] weeks

If Fiona saves £1.20 a week, how many weeks will it be before she can buy:

5 a CD for £8.00?   [ ] weeks

6 a book for £6.35?   [ ] weeks

7 a car kit for £11.50?   [ ] weeks

8 a pair of jeans for £14.80?   [ ] weeks

Name

Points						
Numbers						
1p						
2p						
5p						
10p						
20p						
50p						
£1						
Target						

Name

1 Bob has £5.85. He wants to buy a CD which costs £9.99. How much more money does he need? £ ☐

2 Melons cost 99p each. Jack buys four. How much do they cost altogether? £ ☐

3 What is the cost of five books at four pounds ninety-eight pence each? £ ☐

4 Elin has saved £21.45. She spends five pounds sixty. How much money has she left? £ ☐

5 Ashley pays £22.16 for four tickets. How much each were they? £ ☐

6 Dog food was sixteen pounds fifty-five for a large sack but the price went up by £2.99. What is the new price? £ ☐

69

Know and use the months

Name _____

Which month is:

1 3 months after April _____

2 1 month before June _____

3 2 months after July _____

4 Between December and February _____

5 2 months before August _____

6 6 months after January _____

7 4 months before November _____

8 3 months after June _____

9 5 months before October _____

10 6 months after September _____

Tell the time: analogue/digital

Name _____

Fill in the gaps so the same time is shown in three ways.

1 [clock] | 3:30 | Half past three

2 [clock] | 4:20 | _____

3 [clock] | :: | _____

4 [clock] | :: | Quarter past nine

5 [clock] | 1:55 | _____

70

Set B

1	7:00	→
2	4:30	→
3	6:15	→
4	11:15	→
5	9:30	→
6	8:45	→
7	2:45	→
8	1:15	→
9	10:45	→
10	3:15	→

Set A

1	3:30	→
2	4:00	→
3	7:30	→
4	10:00	→
5	6:30	→
6	2:30	→
7	8:15	→
8	1:30	→
9	5:15	→
10	3:00	→

	Start time	Time taken	Finish time
1	3:00		
2	5:30		
3	6:00		
4	2:30		
5	1:15		
6	7:45		
7	9:30		
8	8:10		
9	10:20		
10	4:40		

Name _____

Change these into hours and minutes

1 65 minutes → [ ] hours [ ] minutes

2 90 minutes → [ ] hours [ ] minutes

3 110 minutes → [ ] hours [ ] minutes

4 125 minutes → [ ] hours [ ] minutes

5 180 minutes → [ ] hours [ ] minutes

Change these into minutes only

6 1 hour 20 minutes → [ ] minutes

7 1 hour 45 minutes → [ ] minutes

8 2 hours 15 minutes → [ ] minutes

9 2 hours 35 minutes → [ ] minutes

10 3 hours 20 minutes → [ ] minutes

Name _____

	12-hour	24-hour
1		
2		
3		
4		
5		

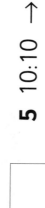

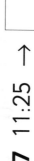
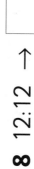

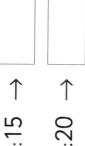

Time C98 — Add and subtract times

Name _____

Set A

☐ minutes earlier

1 3:15 →
2 5:20 →
3 8:10 →
4 6:40 →
5 9:05 →
6 10:35 →
7 11:25 →
8 12:12 →
9 10:45 →
10 7:50 →

Set B

☐ minutes later

1 4:20 →
2 6:25 →
3 7:30 →
4 8:05 →
5 10:10 →
6 12:15 →
7 5:50 →
8 3:45 →
9 1:35 →
10 2:40 →

Time C97 — Use timetables

Name _____

	Train A	Train B	Train C
Westley	09:00	10:40	11:55
Farlen	09:32	11:10	12:23
Barhurst	09:53	11:32	12:45
Redham	10:50	12:29	13:51

1 Which trains arrive at Barhurst before 10:00? _____

2 Which train takes 1 hour 6 minutes to get from Barhurst to Redham? _____

3 How long does train A take to get from Farlen to Barhurst? _____

4 Which train takes 28 minutes to get from Westley to Farlen? _____

5 How long does train B take to get from Westley to Redham? _____

73

Name _____

Continue each time pattern

1 09:30, 09:45, 10:00 ☐ ☐

Pattern **add 15 minutes**

2 06:20, 06:45, 07:10 ☐ ☐

Pattern _____

3 17:05, 17:35, 18:05 ☐ ☐

Pattern _____

4 19:10, 19:25, 19:40 ☐ ☐

Pattern _____

5 22:50, 23:15, 23:40 ☐ ☐

Pattern _____

6 11:45, 12:05, 12:25 ☐ ☐

Pattern _____

Name _____

How long is it from start to finish?

	Start	Finish	Time taken
1	4:15 pm	7:20 pm	
2	2:10 pm	5:25 pm	
3	6:20 pm	7:05 pm	
4	10:30 am	1:15 pm	
5	8:25 am	10:15 am	
6	9:40 am	1:45 pm	
7	7:55 pm	9:40 pm	
8	14:30	17:25	
9	05:20	09:05	
10	16:45	19:35	

Associated Topics

Angles ▷

Shape ▷

Area and Perimeter ▷

Volume and Capacity ▷

Length ▷

Weight ▷

Handling Data ▷

Negative Numbers ▷

Percentages ▷

Name _____

Mark all the angles less than a right angle
with a △

Mark all the angles greater than a right angle
with a ◯

Mark all the right angles with a ✕

Name _____

List the angles in the table

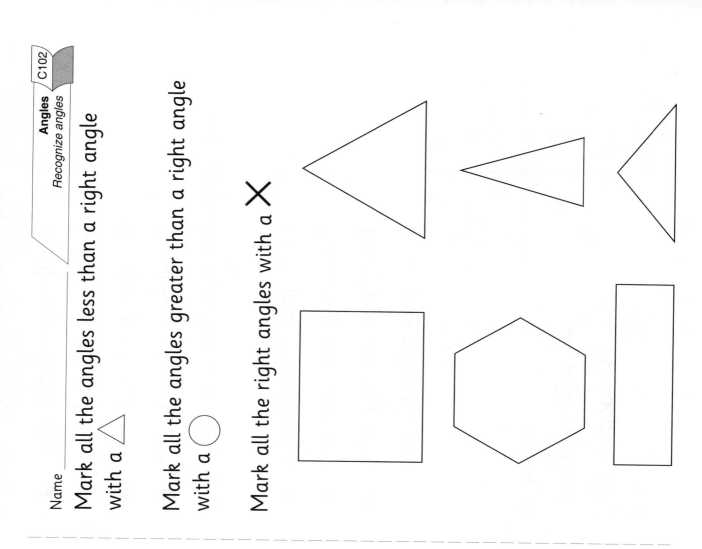

Right angle	Less than right angle	Greater than right angle

77

Name _____

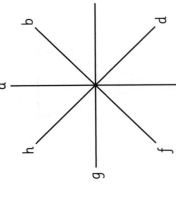

Turn anticlockwise

one-quarter of a turn

each time

1 Start facing g. End facing

2 Start facing c. End facing

3 Start facing a. End facing

4 Start facing d. End facing

Turn clockwise three-quarter turns each time

5 Start facing e. End facing

6 Start facing a. End facing

7 Start facing f. End facing

8 Start facing b. End facing

Name _____

Turn clockwise

How many right angles do I turn through clock-wise?

1 from north to south

2 from west to north

3 from south to east

4 from west to east

5 from north-east to south-east

6 from north-west to north-east

7 from south-east to north-east

8 from north-west to south-east

9 Turn three right angles anticlockwise from

south to face

10 Turn one right angle anticlockwise from

west to face

78

Name

Follow the route
Tick the box if the instructions are correct.
Underline wrong directions.

N

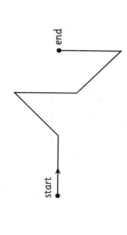

start

end

1 Go east, north-east, south, south-east, north ☐

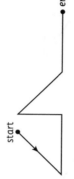

start

end

2 Go south-west, east, north, south-east, west ☐

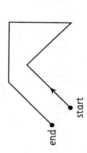

end

start

3 Go north-east, south-east, north, west, south-west ☐

Name

Label acute angles 'a', obtuse angles 'o', reflex
angles 'r' and right angles 'x'

Name _____

Calculate the missing angles

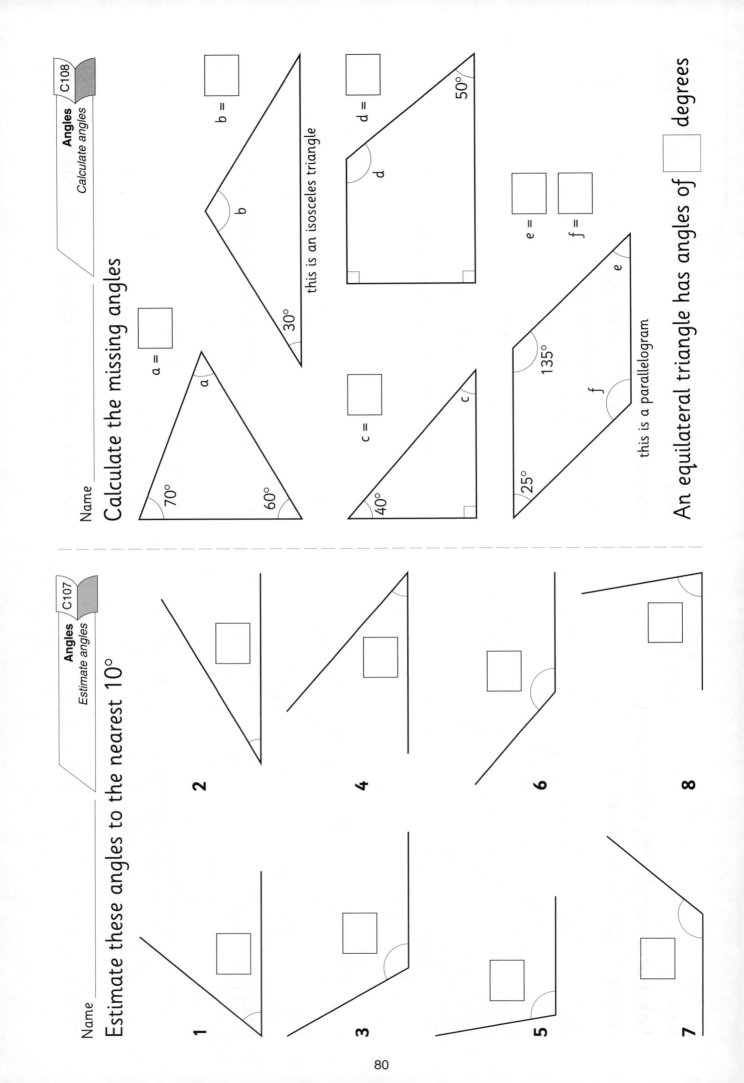

a = ☐

70° a 60°

b = ☐

b 30°

this is an isosceles triangle

c = ☐

40° c

d = ☐

50° d

e = ☐   f = ☐

135°

25° f e

this is a parallelogram

An equilateral triangle has angles of ☐ degrees

Name _____

Estimate these angles to the nearest 10°

1 ☐

2 ☐

3 ☐

4 ☐

5 ☐

6 ☐

7 ☐

8 ☐

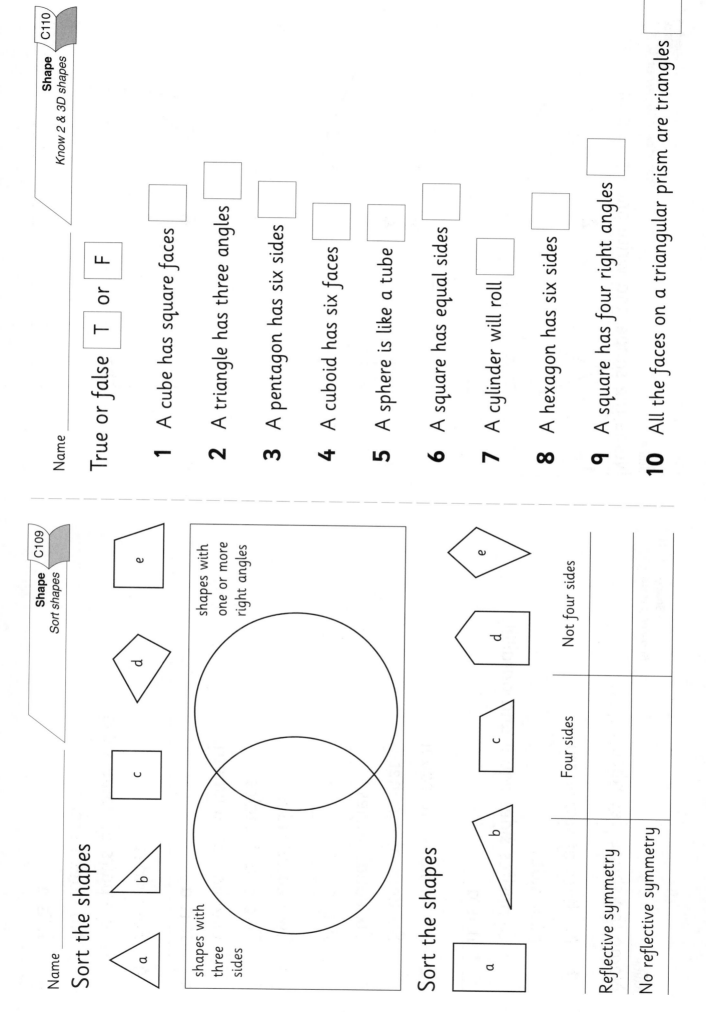

C109 — Shape / Sort shapes

Name ____

Sort the shapes

Shapes: a (triangle), b (triangle), c (square), d (kite/quadrilateral), e (trapezium)

Venn diagram:
- shapes with three sides
- shapes with one or more right angles

Sort the shapes

Shapes: a (square), b (triangle), c (trapezium), d (pentagon), e (kite)

	Four sides	Not four sides
Reflective symmetry		
No reflective symmetry		

C110 — Shape / Know 2 & 3D shapes

Name ____

True or false T or F

1 A cube has square faces ☐

2 A triangle has three angles ☐

3 A pentagon has six sides ☐

4 A cuboid has six faces ☐

5 A sphere is like a tube ☐

6 A square has equal sides ☐

7 A cylinder will roll ☐

8 A hexagon has six sides ☐

9 A square has four right angles ☐

10 All the faces on a triangular prism are triangles ☐

81

Name _____

Name the shape and write one of its properties

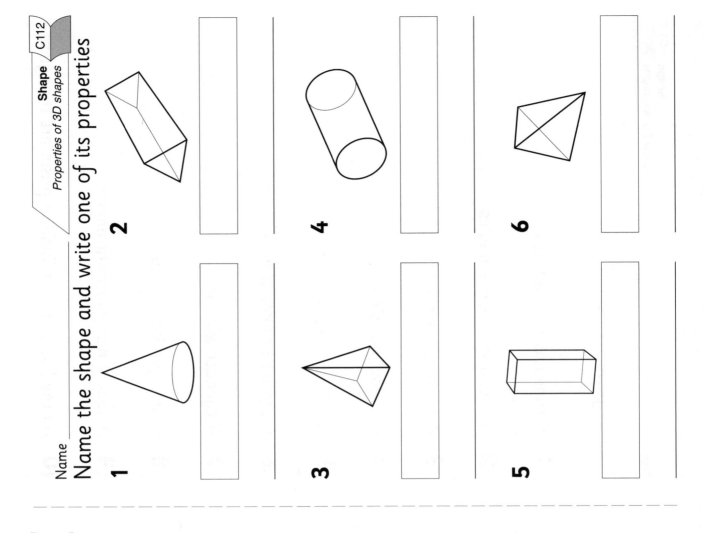

1

2

3

4

5

6

Name _____

Name the shape described

1 No lines of symmetry

Four sides

Opposites sides equal and parallel

It is a _____

2 All its sides are equal

Six lines of symmetry

Six equal angles

It is a _____

3 Two equal sides

Two equal angles

One line of symmetry

It is a _____

4 Four sides

Two pairs of equal sides

No sides parallel

It is a _____

Name _____

1 What is the area of a square with a side of 4 cm?

[ ] cm²

2 A rectangle has an area of 15 cm²

Width = [ ] cm   Length = [ ] cm

3 What is the perimeter of a square with a side of 6 m?

[ ] m

4 A rectangle has a length of 8 m and a width of 6 m

Area = [ ] m²   Perimeter = [ ] m

5 A rectangular field is 125 m long and 75 m wide. How much fencing will be needed to fence all round the perimeter?

[ ] m

6 What is the perimeter of a square with an area of 81 cm²?

P = [ ] cm

Name _____

Work out the area of these shapes

1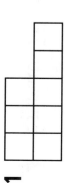

A = [ ] cm²

2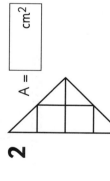

A = [ ] cm²

3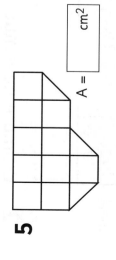

A = [ ] cm²

4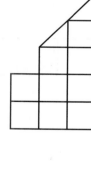

A = [ ] cm²

5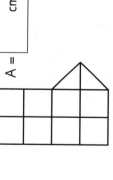

A = [ ] cm²

6

A = [ ] cm²

Work out the perimeter of these.

7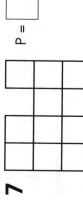

P = [ ] cm

8

P = [ ] cm

1 How many millilitres in a litre?

[ ] ml

2 We have a 2-litre bottle of pop. We drink 500 ml.

How much is left?

[ ]

3 Does a mug hold about 20 ml, 400 ml or 2 litres

of water?

[ ]

4 I have 200 ml of orange, 300 ml of lemon, and

550 ml of pop. Will it all fit in a 1-litre jug?

[ ]

5 How many 1-litre jugs can I fill with 5 000 ml

of water?

[ ]

6 How many 200 ml glasses can I fill from a 2-litre

bottle?

[ ]

---

1 How much is in each container?

300 ml—
200 ml—
100 ml—

[ ] ml

60 ml—
40 ml—
20 ml—

[ ] ml

150 ml—
100 ml—
50 ml—

[ ] ml

2 Estimate how much is in each bottle

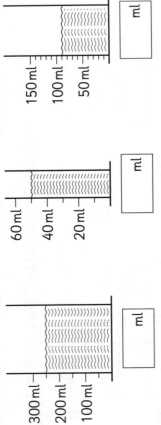

holds
2 litres

[ ]

holds
1 litre

[ ]

holds
1 litre

[ ]

3 Estimate 750 ml in this container

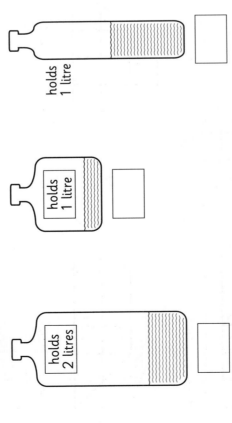

holds 2 litres

84

Name ___

Circle the three measurements of the cuboid to give the correct volume

1 $12\,cm^3$

| 4 cm | 2 cm | 5 cm |
| 3 cm | 7 cm | 1 cm |

2 $18\,cm^3$

| 3 cm | 8 cm | 2 cm |
| 5 cm | 3 cm | 4 cm |

3 $20\,cm^3$

| 2 m | 3 m | 5 m |
| 2 m | 6 m | 1 m |

4 $24\,cm^3$

| 2 m | 1 m | 5 m |
| 3 m | 9 m | 4 m |

5 $32\,cm^3$

| 2 cm | 5 cm | 8 cm |
| 3 cm | 2 cm | 6 cm |

Name ___

What is the volume of these cuboids?

1

volume = [   ] cm^3

2

volume = [   ] cm^3

3

volume = [   ] cm^3

4

volume = [   ] cm^3

5 What is the volume of a box 4 cm wide, 6 cm long and 2 cm high? [   ] cm^3

6 How many 1 cm^3 cubes will fit in a box 3 cm wide, 4 cm long and 10 cm high? [   ]

85

Name _____

1 How many millimetres in 1 centimetre?

☐ mm

2 Alan runs 2000 m. How many kilometres has

he run?

☐ km

3 I walk 500 m, then I walk another 500 m. How far

is that it altogether?

☐ km

4 My book measures 150 mm wide. How wide is it

in centimetres?

☐ cm

5 Jan has 3 metres of ribbon. How many

centimetres long is the ribbon?

☐ cm

6 Bob has a plank 2 metres long. He cuts off 50 cm.

How long is the piece that is left?

☐

Name _____

Estimate the length of these lines

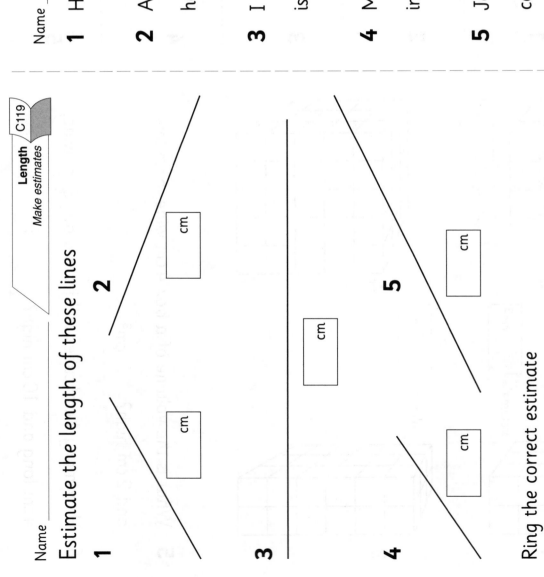

1 ☐ cm

2 ☐ cm

3 ☐ cm

4 ☐ cm

5 ☐ cm

Ring the correct estimate

6 A pen is about   6 cm   14 cm   22 cm   long

7 A car is about   1 m   3 m   10 m   long

8 A door is about   2 m   5 m   10 m   high

Name _____

Match equal lengths
(They do not all have partners)

20 cm

2000 m

2 m

200 cm

20 km

2 km

35 mm

3·5 cm

35 cm

350 cm

3·5 km

$3\frac{1}{2}$ m

350 m

3500 m

Name _____

True or false T or F

1 1 metre is roughly 3 feet ☐

2 5 miles is roughly 1 kilometre ☐

3 1 foot is roughly 30 cm ☐

Solve these problems

4 A ribbon 2 metres long is cut into four equal pieces. Each piece is ☐ long.

5 130 cm is cut off a 2-metre plank. How much is left? ☐

6 Fred runs 1·2 km. How many metres is that? ☐ m

7 Fence panels are 1·5 m wide. How many are needed to fence 9 m? ☐

8 Rosie walks 5·4 km of a 9 km hike. How many metres has she left to walk? ☐ m

Name _____

Ring the most sensible estimate

1 A jar of jam	5 g	500 g	5 kg
2 An apple	10 g	150 g	1 kg
3 A toy car	10 g	100 g	10 kg
4 A dining-room chair	5 g	5 kg	50 kg
5 An eight-year-old boy	2 kg	5 kg	25 kg
6 A comic	5 g	50 g	5 kg
7 A packet of crisps	1 g	25 g	1 kg
8 An empty lunch box	300 g	30 kg	3 g
9 A cat	30 g	3 kg	30 kg
10 A tall, thin man	70 g	7 kg	70 kg

88

Name _____

1 Oranges weigh about 200 g each. How many weigh

about 1 kg? ☐

2 Billy weighs 28 kg. His sister weighs 31 kg.

When his dad lifts them both, how much is he

lifting? ☐ kg

3 Sue uses 500 g from a 1 kg bag of sugar. How much

is left? ☐ g

4 How many grams in 4 kg? ☐ g

5 Four friends share 1 kg of sweets equally. How much

do they each get? ☐ g

6 How much do seven 500 g jars of pickle weigh

together? ☐

Match pairs that add to make 2 kg

1·50 kg

1250 g

0·75 kg

1400 g

1·20 kg

500 g

250 g

800 g

0·60 kg

1750 g

Match pairs that have a difference of 200 g

1·20 kg

1360 g

1·56 kg

4·90 kg

1000 g

2 kg

5 100 g

5·90 kg

6·10 kg

1·80 kg

---

1 Change 1 kilogram into grams. ⬚ g

2 Change 4 kilograms into grams. ⬚ g

3 Change 6 000 grams into kg. ⬚ kg

4 Change $3\frac{1}{2}$ kilograms into grams. ⬚ g

5 Change $2\frac{1}{4}$ kilograms into grams. ⬚ g

6 1 kilogram is roughly ⬚ pounds.

7 1 stone is roughly ⬚ kilograms.

8 100 grams is roughly ⬚ ounces.

Name _____

What is the mean?

1 3, 4, 8   Mean = ☐

2 5, 2, 2   Mean = ☐

3 4, 6, 3, 3   Mean = ☐

4 7, 8, 3, 2, 5   Mean = ☐

Fill in the missing number to make the mean correct.

5 4, 11, ☐   Mean = 7

6 8, 3, 12, ☐   Mean = 6

7 9, 4, 7, 6, ☐   Mean = 6

8 Five cricketers have a mean score of 21 runs. Four of them have scored 27, 19, 20 and 22. What is the fifth one's score? ☐

Name _____

What is the mode of each set?

1 3, 4, 7, 4, 6, 4, 3   Mode = ☐

2 21, 19, 21, 18, 17, 21   Mode = ☐

3 B, B, A, C, A, B, C   Mode = ☐

4 13, 14, 15, 14, 16, 15, 14   Mode = ☐

Is the median circled? ✓ or ✗

5 1, 1, 2, ③, 7, 8, 9   ☐

6 15, 17, ⑰, 18, 19, 22, 24   ☐

7 7, 7, 7, ⑧, 8, 9, 9   ☐

8 4, 5, ⑤, 5, 6   ☐

9 In a group of friends, four people wear size 4 shoes, three people wear size 5, and two people wear size 6.

Which size is the mode? ☐

Which size is the median? ☐

90

Name _____

Write the answers as fractions. If a dice is thrown

what is the probability of getting

□ □ □ □ □

1 an even number?

2 a three?

3 an odd number?

4 a multiple of three?

5 a number less than six?

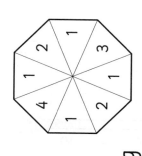

Look at the spinner.

What is the probability of spinning

6 a one?

7 an even number?

8 a two?

Name _____

From a pack of 10 cards numbered 1 to 10, label

these probabilities on the line

```
1 ─┬─
   │
   ┼
   │
   ┼
   │
   ┼
   │
   ┼
   │
0 ─┴─
```

Plot the probability of picking

A An odd number

B A five

C A number greater than 10

D A number less than five

E A multiple of three

F A number greater than three

91

Name _____

What is the temperature?

1 [°C]

2 [°C]

3 [°C]

Use RISE or FALL

4 The temperature in the morning is −2°C. By lunch time it is 4°C. This is a [ ] of [ ] °C.

5 At night the temperature was −5°C. In the day it was 16°C. This is a [ ] of [ ] °C.

6 At midday the temperature was 14°C. At night it was −3°C. This is a [ ] of [ ] °C.

Name _____

The first dice throw moves you forwards.
The second dice throw moves you backwards.

What number do you end on?

	start	1st throw	2nd throw	end
1	6			
2	5			
3	3			
4	9			
5	4			
6	2			
7	3			
8	1			

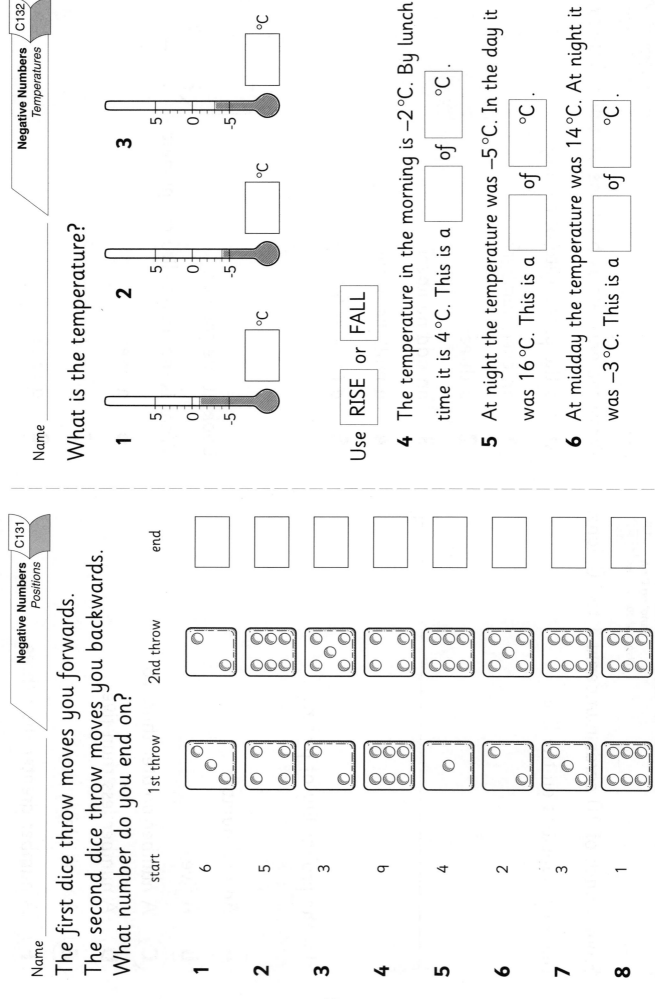

Name

The chart shows temperatures taken for five days and nights.

	Mon	Tues	Wed	Thurs	Fri
day	3°C	5°C	8°C	4°C	6°C
night	–5°C	–7°C	–9°C	–1°C	1°C

1 Which was the coldest night? _____

2 Which was the warmest night? _____

3 Which day did the temperature fall by 12°C? _____

4 Which daytime temperature was 13°C warmer than Tuesday night? _____

5 Put the night-time temperatures in order coldest first _____

6 By how much did the temperature fall on Wednesday? _____

Name

Each player throws a dice and picks a card. The dice is a positive number the card is a negative number. Work out each player's score.

Player	Dice	Card	Score
Ann	5	7	
Bill	3	4	
Carl	6	5	
Debbie	4	10	
Eric	2	6	
Fay	1	3	

1 Who scores more than Ann? _____

2 Which two score the same? _____ and _____

3 Who scores less than Eric? _____

4 What card should Debbie have picked to score the same as Eric? _____

Match the ones that mean the same

50%

0.75

$\frac{3}{4}$

$\frac{1}{2}$ 75%

0.5

$\frac{5}{10}$ 0.1

25%

$\frac{1}{4}$

$\frac{25}{100}$

$\frac{50}{100}$

0.25

$\frac{1}{10}$

10%

$\frac{75}{100}$

$\frac{10}{100}$

Put ✓ or ✗

1 $0.4 = \frac{4}{10} = 40\%$

2 $\frac{1}{4} = 0.25 = 25\%$

3 $\frac{1}{5} = 0.15 = 15\%$

4 $0.75 = \frac{3}{4} = 75\%$

5 $\frac{50}{100} = 50\% = 0.5 = \frac{1}{2}$

6 $20\% = 0.02 = \frac{2}{100} = \frac{1}{50}$

7 $0.1 = \frac{1}{10} = \frac{10}{100} = 10\%$

8 $\frac{9}{10} = \frac{90}{100} = 90\% = 0.9$

9 $\frac{3}{10} = 0.3 = \frac{30}{100} = 30\%$

☐ ☐ ☐ ☐ ☐ ☐ ☐ ☐ ☐

Name _____

1 A dress costing £42.50 is reduced by 10%.

What is the sale price? £ [ ]

2 The price of a £9650 car goes up by 20%.

How much does it cost now? £ [ ]

3 Take 75% off each of these:

£48 [ ]

£5.60 [ ]

£3.24 [ ]

£720 [ ]

4 25% of a number is 17.

What is the number? [ ]

5 40% of a number is 32.

What is the number? [ ]

6 Add 20% to each of these:

120 [ ]

340 [ ]

Name _____

Fill in the missing numbers

	10%	20%	50%
1 30	3		
2 80		16	
3 40			20
4 22			
5 64			

	25%	50%	75%
6 40			30
7 60			
8 124			
9 240			
10 36			

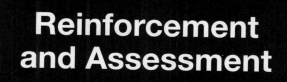

Reinforcement and Assessment

Topic Tests ▷

Recall Practice ▷

Quick Maths ▷

Key Stage 2 Practice Tests ▷

Level 3

Level 4/5

Level 5

1 Is it sensible to say that a man weighs 4 kilograms?

2 What units would you use to weigh an apple?

3 Take 15 away from 36.

4 What number is 22 less than 45?

5 How many grams are there in a kilogram? g

6 Subtract 71 from 100.

7 How many kg is 4000 g? kg

8 A bag of flour weighed 1 kilogram. Half of it was used. How many grams of flour were left? g

9 How many grams are there in 3 kilograms? g

10 75 – 59 =

11 Subtract 68 from 85.

12 How many more than 36 is 64?

13 Is it sensible to say that an apple weighs 120 g?

14 A man weighs 81 kg. He goes on a diet and loses 13 kg. How much does he weigh now? kg

15 A wheelbarrow contains 56 kg of sand and 29 kg is used. How much is left? kg

1 What number is one more than 69?

2 What number is one less than 500?

3 Add 10 to 146.

4 Subtract 10 from 908.

5 It is 100 miles to Fenbury. I have gone 43 miles. How much further have I to go?

6 Plot the number 40 on this number line.

0 ——————————————————————— 100

7 What is 545 to the nearest hundred?

8 Add 57 to 34.

9 Write two hundred and six in figures.

10 What is the sum of 7, 9 and 4?

11 Put the numbers in order smallest first.
67, 209, 129, 902, 99, 301 ———————————————

12 What is an approximate answer to 41 + 37?

13 Choose three of these digits to make the largest possible number.   5, 9, 3, 8

14 Add 10 to 395.

15 What number is 100 less than 426?

Name _____

1 How many centimetres in 4 metres? ☐ cm

2 What is 3·4 to the nearest whole one? ☐

3 What units would you use to measure the length of the classroom? ☐

4 What number is one-tenth more than 2·9? ☐

5 Estimate the length of this line. _____ ☐ cm

6 Bill is 1·25 m tall. He grows ten centimetres. How tall is he now? ☐ m

7 A ribbon 1 metre long is cut into four equal pieces. How long is each piece? ☐ cm

8 Is 35 mm a good estimate for the length of a book? ☐

9 Write three-tenths as a decimal number. ☐

10 What number is five-tenths less than five? ☐

11 My bedroom is 3·5 m long. I have a piece of carpet 4 m long. How many centimetres of carpet do I need to cut off? ☐ cm

12 Add three-tenths to 2·4. ☐

13 How many millimetres in $5\frac{1}{2}$ centimetres? ☐ mm

14 Subtract four-tenths from 5·3. ☐

15 Jill runs in a 5-kilometre race. When she has run 4·5 km how many more metres has she left to run? ☐ m

1   Draw a line of symmetry on this shape.

2   How many right angles has a rectangle?

3   I have three 50-pence coins and two 20-pence coins.
    How much is that?   £ _____

4   How could you pay 71 pence exactly using three coins?

    [ ] p   [ ] p   [ ] p

5   Write three pounds and four pence as it would appear on
    a calculator.   [_____]

6   What is this shape?   _____

7   Draw a line of symmetry on this shape.

8   What is a shape with six equal sides called? _____

9   What is the total cost of five sweets at 8 pence each?   [ ] p

10 If you have £1 and spend 64 pence, how much do
    you have left?   [ ] p

11 What shape are the faces of a cube? _____

12 Name this shape.   _____

13 How many sides does a triangle have?   [ ]

14 What is the change from £2.00 if I spend £1.38?   [ ] p

15 What change do I get from £5.00 if I spend £3.71?   £ [ ]

1 Multiply nine by two. ☐

2 Divide 30 by five. ☐

3 What is the remainder when 42 is divided by 10? ☐

4 $10 \times 6 =$ ☐

5 How many millilitres in a litre? ☐ ml

6 Is it sensible to say a glass holds 400 ml? ☐

7 Half a 1-litre bottle of lemonade has gone. How many millilitres are left? ☐ ml

8 What is the remainder when 37 is divided by 5? ☐

9 $5 \times 9 =$ ☐

10 Spiders have eight legs. How many legs on five spiders? ☐

11 Lucy saves £4 a week for four weeks. How much has she saved? £☐

12 How many more millilitres are needed to make 750 ml up to 1 litre? ☐ ml

13 There are four cars and 23 people. Five people can fit in each car. How many people are left over? ☐

14 Divide 62 by 10. ☐

15 Is it sensible to say a teaspoon holds 200 ml? ☐

Name _____

1 What is half of 18? ☐

2 What comes next?   2, 5, 8, 11, ____

3 On a calculator I enter five, then add six. What do I need to do to get back to five? _____

4 In a board game a counter is on 12. If it moves back four where does it land? ☐

5 What is the temperature? 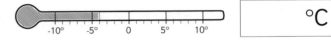 ☐ °C

6 What is double eight? ☐

7 What comes next?   3, 7, 11, 15, ____

8 What is the temperature? 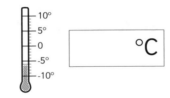 ☐ °C

9 I enter six on the calculator then subtract five. How do I get a six in the display again? _____

10 What is half of 24? ☐

11 Which is warmer, −3 degrees Celsius or 2 degrees Celsius? ☐ °C

12 What is double 14? ☐

13 A number machine subtracts eight from any numbers that are put into it. If 16 is put in, what comes out? ☐

14 What comes next?   19, 16, 13, 10, ____

15 A number has seven added to it to make 15. What was the number? ☐

1 What is one-tenth more than 4·9?

2 Write six-tenths as a decimal number.

3 What is half of 10?

4 What is half of 18?

5 Add 1·2 and 5·6.

6 What is a quarter of 16?

7 What is a quarter of 40?

8 How many equal parts are there if a ribbon is cut into thirds?

9 Subtract three-tenths from 6·7.

10 If a rope is cut into five equal parts what is one part called? _____

11 Write a half as a decimal.

12 What is a quarter of £2.00?

13 What is half of £5.00?

14 Shade one-third of this shape.

15 What fraction is not shaded?

Name _____

1 What direction is opposite north? _____

2 I face west and make one right-angle turn clockwise. Which direction am I facing now? _____

3 What time is this? _____

4 Write this time in words   10:15 _____

5 What month is three months after May? _____

6 Is 8:15 pm a sensible time to have breakfast? _____

7 How many minutes are there in one hour?

8 How many days are there in three weeks?

9 How many days are there in March?

10 How many right angles does a square have?

11 Is this angle bigger or smaller than a right angle?

_____

12 Mark an angle bigger than a right angle on this shape.

13 How long is it from 9:30 to 11:45? _____

14 What time is it?

15 I face north-west and make a quarter turn anticlockwise. In which direction am I facing now? _____

1 What is the area of this shape?  cm²

2 What is the median number? 4, 7, 9, 12, 13 ☐

3 What is the perimeter of this shape?

 cm

4 What is the mode of these numbers?

5, 6, 8, 5, 3, 5, 9, 8 ☐

5 What is the area of this shape?  cm²

6 Write a group of five numbers which have 6 as their mode.

_____

7 What is the perimeter of this shape?  cm

8 Write a group of seven numbers which have a median of 5.

_____

9 What is the area of a square with sides 4 metres long?

☐ m²

10 What is the perimeter of a rectangle 10 centimetres long and 4 centimetres wide? ☐ cm

Name

1 Continue this pattern.   76 86 96 ___ ___

2 Write the number thirty thousand and ten in figures.

3 Multiply 20 by 100.

4 What is 100 less than 4062?

5 What is 6576 to the nearest thousand?

6 Multiply 65 by 10.

7 In a large hall there were 100 rows of chairs with 47 chairs in each row. How many chairs were there altogether?

8 Divide 9400 by 100.

9 Approximately what is the answer when 149 is added to 352?

10 What is 5000 divided by 10?

1 What is 50% of 240 cm? ▭ cm

2 Write 50 per cent as a decimal. ▭

3 What is three-quarters of 24? ▭

4 In a class of 32, one-quarter are girls.
How many are boys? ▭

5 Multiply 3·5 by 100. ▭

6 Is 5 out of 25 the same as one-fifth? ▭

7 What is 25% of £400? £ ▭

8 Is 40 out of 60 the same as two-thirds? ▭

9 Divide 4·2 by 10. ▭

10 What is 75% of £280? £ ▭

Name _____

1 Write five past eight as it would appear on a digital watch.

2 In a parallelogram, how many angles are bigger than a right angle?

3 Write 20 to 9 as it would appear on a digital watch.

4 How long is it from 13:15 to 15:30? _____

5 What is 4:25 pm in 24-hour time?

6 Draw the time 17:35 on this clock.

7 John starts washing the car at 10:50 am. It takes him 25 minutes. At what time does he finish? _____

8 Sarah arrived at school at five past nine. The journey had taken 20 minutes. At what time did she set off?

_____

9 How many seconds in $2\frac{1}{4}$ minutes?

10 What direction is half a right angle clockwise from south?

_____

1 $7 \times 7 =$ ☐

2 42 divided by 8 = ☐

3 A number multiplied by three is 90. What is the number?

☐

4 A number divided by 4 is 20. What is the number?

☐

5 What is the volume of this shape? ☐ cm^3

6 This box can hold 50 centimetre cubes.

How wide is it? ☐ cm

7 If four identical glasses hold 1600 ml, how much will three

glasses hold? ☐ ml

8 $40 \times 60 =$ ☐

9 How many fours in 320? ☐

10 Three different mugs hold a total of 1 litre. Two hold 230 ml

and 450 ml. How much does the third one hold? ☐ ml

1   Put these numbers in order of size, smallest first.

5, 4·9, 5·4, 4·5 _____

2   How many metres in 0·4 km? ☐ m

3   4·3 added to a number makes 10. What is the number?

☐

4   How many cm in 0·7 m? ☐ cm

5   By how much is 5·7 more than 4·8? ☐

6   A rope 5 m long is cut into four equal pieces. How long is each piece? ☐

7   Multiply 6·4 by 10. ☐

8   Divide 50 m by 100. ☐

9   What is half of 3·5 km? ☐

10   What is 4·7 multiplied by 100? ☐

1 Four children each spend £5.99. How much is that altogether?

£ _____

2 If a rope 2·6 metres long is cut into five equal pieces how long will each piece be? _____

3 Two buses take some people on a trip. There are 58 people on one bus and 39 people on the other. How many people go on the trip? _____

4 On three days the number of people in the audience at a play were 345, 264 and 283. Altogether how many people watched the play? _____

5 Angela won £3560. She spent £1555 on a holiday. How much has she got left? £ _____

6 Nine people share £810 equally. How much do they each receive? £ _____

7 Chris has £5.68 and wants to buy a CD for £12.99. How much more money does he need? £ _____

8 A book costs £6.50. Nick saves 70 pence a week. How many weeks before he can buy it? _____

9 How much will seven videos at £9.99 cost? £ _____

10 There are 307 pupils at a school and 158 are girls. How many are boys? _____

1 What is the next square number after 25? ☐

2 List the factors of 21. _____

3 Is 72 a multiple of three? ☐

4 What temperature is 3 degrees Celsius colder than 2 degrees Celsius? ☐ °C

5 The temperature rises 5 degrees Celsius from −4 degrees Celsius. What is the new temperature? ☐ °C

6 List all the factors of 24. _____

7 What is the next square number after 81? ☐

8 List the multiples of 12 between 50 and 100. _____

9 What comes next?   1, 3, 6, 10, 15, __

10 Start with seven. Double it and subtract three. What is the new number? ☐

1 How could you pay £2.89 exactly using eight coins?

_____

2 Divide £10 by 8. £ [   ]

3 Multiply £4.25 by 6. £ [   ]

4 How many sides has a quadrilateral? [   ]

5 Does a kite have a line of symmetry? [   ]

6 Name the shape this net would make.

_____

7 Add together 75 pence, £3.08 and 20 pence. £ [   ]

8 What is the cost of four books at £2.99 each? £ [   ]

9 What is a triangle with all its sides equal called?

_____

10 What shape has two triangular faces and three rectangular faces? _____

Name _____

1　Subtract 345 from 849. ☐

2　Take 257 from 788. ☐

3　How many grams in $3\frac{1}{2}$ kilograms? ☐ g

4　How many grams in a quarter of a kilogram? ☐ g

5　I buy 1·4 kg of apples, 2·5 kg of pears and 5·3 kg of potatoes. How much do they weigh altogether? ☐ kg

6　I need 2 kilograms of strawberries to make jam. I pick 1·48 kg. How many more grams of strawberries do I need? ☐ g

7　What number is 178 less than 435? ☐

8　Write 5 550 g as kg. ☐ kg

9　A trolley can carry 500 kg. How many complete crates weighing 75 kg each can it hold? ☐

10　For a recipe, Jane uses three packets of oranges and lemons each weighing 85 g. What is the total weight she uses? ☐ g

1 When I woke up, the temperature was −3 degrees Celsius. By lunch time, it was 5 degrees Celsius. By how many degrees Celsius has it risen? [   ] °C

2 I think of a number, multiply it by three then add five to get 26. What was the number? [   ]

3 I set off on a journey at 10 past 11 in the morning and arrive at 14:05. How long did the journey take? _____

4 Three angles of a quadrilateral add up to 265 degrees. What is the fourth angle? [   ]

5 What is the area of a square with a perimeter of 28 cm? [   ] cm²

6 4 kg of potatoes cost £2.40. How much will 7 kg cost? £ [   ]

7 In a test, Susan needs 60% to pass. She gets 46 marks out of 80. Does she pass? [   ]

8 When you roll a dice, what is the probability of getting an even number? [   ]

9 What is the perimeter of a square with an area of 64 square centimetres? [   ] cm

10 How many edges does a square-based pyramid have? [   ]

Name _____

1 Five oranges cost £1.25, how much would three cost?

2 Multiply £3.45 by 3. £ [ ]

3 What is the order of rotation of an equilateral triangle?

4 How many edges does this shape have? [ ]

5 I have 70 pence a week for tidying my room. How much will I have after eight weeks? £ [ ]

6 1 kg of apples costs £1.06. How much will $\frac{1}{2}$ kilogram cost?

7 How many vertices has a cube? [ ]

8 What type of symmetry does a parallelogram have? _____

9 What is this shape? _____

10 When £22 is shared equally between a group of children they get £2.75 each. How many children are there?

1 What is 5·2 divided by 1000? ⬚

2 What is 30% of £80? £ ⬚

3 20% of a number is 12. What is the number? ⬚

4 Three-fifths of a number is 21. What is the number? ⬚

5 Multiply 0·09 by 1000. ⬚

6 What is 40% of £320? £ ⬚

7 Out of 24 eggs, two-thirds are cracked. How many are not cracked? ⬚

8 In a test, Alan needs 75% to pass. He gets 47 marks out of 60. Does he pass? ⬚

9 How many centimetres in three-fifths of a metre? ⬚ cm

10 What number is halfway between 8·5 and 14·5? ⬚

1   Is this angle acute or obtuse?    _____

2   Estimate to the nearest 10 degrees the size of the angle in question 1.

3   Two angles of a triangle add up to 130 degrees. What is the size of the third angle?

4   How many minutes in $3\frac{1}{4}$ hours?

5   A train arrives at 14:03. It is 15 minutes late. At what time should it have arrived?

6   An isosceles triangle has one angle of 40 degrees. The other two angles are equal. What size are they? each.

7   Three angles of a quadrilateral add up to 250 degrees. What is the size of the fourth angle?

8   What is the size of angle a?   52° a

9   The 09:40 bus sets off on a journey that takes $4\frac{1}{2}$ hours. What time does it arrive?

10   Estimate the size of this angle to the nearest 10 degrees.

1 Put these temperatures in order, coldest first.

5, –1, 9, 0, –3, _____

2 In the morning, the temperature is –4 degrees Celsius. What is the temperature after a rise of 8 degrees Celsius?

☐ °C

3 What is the temperature change from 4 degrees Celsius to –2 degrees Celsius? _____

4 I think of a number and double it. I get 26. What was my number? ☐

5 I think of a number, add four then halve it. I get five. What was my number? ☐

6 Given this formula, P = (R × 2) + 2, if R = 4 work out what P is.

☐

7 Given this formula, P = (R × 3) – 4, if R = 2 work out what P is.

☐

8 Write these numbers in order, smallest first.

–2, 6, 4, –5, –1 _____

9 What is the fall in temperature from 3 degrees Celsius to –4 degrees Celsius? ☐ °C

10 I add four to a number then multiply the answer by five to get 45. What was the number? ☐

Name

Addition Grid 1

Date

+	4	2	7	3	6	5
1						
4						
2						
5						
3						

$\overline{30}$

Time: ____

Addition Grid 2

Date

+	5	3	7	4	9	6
2						
8						
6						
10						
7						

$\overline{30}$

Time: ____

Addition Grid 3

Date

+	8	12	9	11	13	6	10	7
10								
7								
12								
9								
11								
6								
8								
5								

$\overline{64}$

Time: ____

Addition Grid 4

Date

+	13	24	16	18	21	17	23	25
14								
19								
21								
18								
15								
17								
25								
16								

$\overline{64}$

Time: ____

Subtraction Grid 1

Date _____

−	8	11	7	9	6	10
6						
3						
5						
2						
4						

$\overline{30}$

Time: ____

Subtraction Grid 2

Date _____

−	18	20	16	19	15	17
8						
13						
9						
12						
7						

$\overline{30}$

Time: ____

Name

Subtraction Grid 3

Date

−	20	23	19	25	18	24	22	17
10								
6								
7								
9								
12								
8								
13								
16								

$\overline{64}$

Time: ____

Subtraction Grid 4

Date

−	45	37	42	36	41	39	44	35
17								
19								
26								
15								
27								
18								
16								
29								

$\overline{64}$

Time: ____

Multiplication Grid 1

Date

×	2	5	8	1	3	6	9	10	7	4
2										
5										
10										

$\overline{30}$ Time: _____

Multiplication Grid 2

Date

×	2	5	0	4	10	3
2						
10						
3						
5						
4						

$\overline{30}$

Time: _____

Multiplication Grid 3

Date

×	2	5	10	3	9	4	6	8
2								
5								
10								
3								
9								
4								
6								
7								

$\overline{64}$

Time: ____

Multiplication Grid 4

Date

×	6	4	9	8	5	11	7	12
6								
4								
9								
8								
5								
11								
7								
12								

$\overline{64}$

Time: ____

Name _____

Set A   Date _____

1   $3 + 1 =$ [ ]   11 $7 + 1 =$ [ ]

2   $4 + 2 =$ [ ]   12 $4 + 3 =$ [ ]

3   $6 + 1 =$ [ ]   13 $7 + 2 =$ [ ]

4   $8 + 2 =$ [ ]   14 $5 + 3 =$ [ ]

5   $4 + 1 =$ [ ]   15 $8 + 1 =$ [ ]

6   $3 + 3 =$ [ ]   16 $3 + 2 =$ [ ]

7   $5 + 1 =$ [ ]   17 $5 + 2 =$ [ ]

8   $6 + 2 =$ [ ]   18 $3 + 4 =$ [ ]

9   $9 + 1 =$ [ ]   19 $5 + 5 =$ [ ]

10   $2 + 3 =$ [ ]   20 $4 + 4 =$ [ ]

Set B   Date _____

1   $2 + 2 =$ [ ]   11 $2 + 4 =$ [ ]

2   $1 + 5 =$ [ ]   12 $1 + 8 =$ [ ]

3   $2 + 6 =$ [ ]   13 $4 + 6 =$ [ ]

4   $3 + 4 =$ [ ]   14 $2 + 3 =$ [ ]

5   $2 + 5 =$ [ ]   15 $3 + 3 =$ [ ]

6   $3 + 6 =$ [ ]   16 $1 + 6 =$ [ ]

7   $1 + 7 =$ [ ]   17 $3 + 7 =$ [ ]

8   $2 + 8 =$ [ ]   18 $1 + 4 =$ [ ]

9   $3 + 5 =$ [ ]   19 $3 + 2 =$ [ ]

10   $2 + 7 =$ [ ]   20 $1 + 9 =$ [ ]

Set C   Date _____

1   $6 - 1 =$ [ ]   11 $9 - 1 =$ [ ]

2   $8 - 2 =$ [ ]   12 $10 - 3 =$ [ ]

3   $7 - 3 =$ [ ]   13 $8 - 1 =$ [ ]

4   $5 - 1 =$ [ ]   14 $6 - 2 =$ [ ]

5   $9 - 2 =$ [ ]   15 $9 - 3 =$ [ ]

6   $8 - 3 =$ [ ]   16 $7 - 2 =$ [ ]

7   $4 - 1 =$ [ ]   17 $10 - 1 =$ [ ]

8   $10 - 2 =$ [ ]   18 $5 - 2 =$ [ ]

9   $6 - 3 =$ [ ]   19 $8 - 4 =$ [ ]

10   $7 - 1 =$ [ ]   20 $5 - 3 =$ [ ]

Set D   Date _____

1   $8 - 5 =$ [ ]   11 $10 - 6 =$ [ ]

2   $9 - 8 =$ [ ]   12 $7 - 5 =$ [ ]

3   $6 - 4 =$ [ ]   13 $9 - 7 =$ [ ]

4   $9 - 5 =$ [ ]   14 $10 - 9 =$ [ ]

5   $10 - 7 =$ [ ]   15 $9 - 6 =$ [ ]

6   $9 - 4 =$ [ ]   16 $6 - 5 =$ [ ]

7   $10 - 5 =$ [ ]   17 $8 - 7 =$ [ ]

8   $8 - 4 =$ [ ]   18 $7 - 4 =$ [ ]

9   $10 - 8 =$ [ ]   19 $10 - 4 =$ [ ]

10   $7 - 6 =$ [ ]   20 $8 - 6 =$ [ ]

Name _____

Set A   Date _____

1	6 + 6 =	**11**	5 + 9 =
2	7 + 8 =	**12**	6 + 5 =
3	8 + 4 =	**13**	7 + 6 =
4	9 + 6 =	**14**	6 + 9 =
5	7 + 7 =	**15**	8 + 5 =
6	8 + 6 =	**16**	9 + 5 =
7	7 + 4 =	**17**	6 + 7 =
8	5 + 6 =	**18**	8 + 7 =
9	8 + 8 =	**19**	7 + 5 =
10	9 + 4 =	**20**	6 + 8 =

Set B   Date _____

1	12 + 7 =	**11**	17 + 3 =
2	14 + 6 =	**12**	12 + 8 =
3	9 + 9 =	**13**	8 + 11 =
4	8 + 12 =	**14**	9 + 7 =
5	8 + 9 =	**15**	4 + 16 =
6	7 + 13 =	**16**	13 + 7 =
7	6 + 12 =	**17**	7 + 9 =
8	9 + 8 =	**18**	14 + 5 =
9	16 + 4 =	**19**	9 + 10 =
10	13 + 6 =	**20**	15 + 5 =

Set C   Date _____

1	14 − 6 =	**11**	13 − 6 =
2	12 − 7 =	**12**	14 − 8 =
3	13 − 8 =	**13**	12 − 8 =
4	15 − 7 =	**14**	15 − 6 =
5	14 − 9 =	**15**	13 − 5 =
6	12 − 6 =	**16**	14 − 7 =
7	13 − 7 =	**17**	12 − 4 =
8	15 − 8 =	**18**	15 − 9 =
9	11 − 8 =	**19**	13 − 4 =
10	12 − 5 =	**20**	14 − 5 =

Set D   Date _____

1	16 − 7 =	**11**	19 − 11 =
2	18 − 9 =	**12**	17 − 5 =
3	17 − 8 =	**13**	18 − 6 =
4	19 − 12 =	**14**	20 − 14 =
5	16 − 8 =	**15**	19 − 8 =
6	18 − 11 =	**16**	17 − 9 =
7	20 − 6 =	**17**	18 − 12 =
8	19 − 7 =	**18**	20 − 5 =
9	16 − 9 =	**19**	19 − 13 =
10	17 − 6 =	**20**	20 − 12 =

Name

Set A Date

1	$1 \times 3 =$ ☐	**11**	$10 \times 5 =$ ☐
2	$3 \times 2 =$ ☐	**12**	$8 \times 2 =$ ☐
3	$2 \times 5 =$ ☐	**13**	$5 \times 5 =$ ☐
4	$9 \times 2 =$ ☐	**14**	$8 \times 5 =$ ☐
5	$7 \times 5 =$ ☐	**15**	$7 \times 2 =$ ☐
6	$4 \times 2 =$ ☐	**16**	$4 \times 3 =$ ☐
7	$3 \times 5 =$ ☐	**17**	$10 \times 2 =$ ☐
8	$3 \times 3 =$ ☐	**18**	$4 \times 5 =$ ☐
9	$5 \times 2 =$ ☐	**19**	$6 \times 2 =$ ☐
10	$6 \times 5 =$ ☐	**20**	$9 \times 5 =$ ☐

Set B Date

1	$2 \times 8 =$ ☐	**11**	$7 \times 10 =$ ☐
2	$5 \times 5 =$ ☐	**12**	$4 \times 10 =$ ☐
3	$2 \times 6 =$ ☐	**13**	$4 \times 4 =$ ☐
4	$3 \times 2 =$ ☐	**14**	$5 \times 6 =$ ☐
5	$5 \times 8 =$ ☐	**15**	$5 \times 3 =$ ☐
6	$5 \times 2 =$ ☐	**16**	$9 \times 10 =$ ☐
7	$3 \times 4 =$ ☐	**17**	$2 \times 4 =$ ☐
8	$5 \times 9 =$ ☐	**18**	$8 \times 10 =$ ☐
9	$2 \times 10 =$ ☐	**19**	$5 \times 7 =$ ☐
10	$5 \times 4 =$ ☐	**20**	$2 \times 9 =$ ☐

Set C Date

1	$20 \div 5 =$ ☐	**11**	$20 \div 2 =$ ☐
2	$4 \div 2 =$ ☐	**12**	$30 \div 5 =$ ☐
3	$25 \div 5 =$ ☐	**13**	$14 \div 2 =$ ☐
4	$10 \div 2 =$ ☐	**14**	$45 \div 5 =$ ☐
5	$15 \div 5 =$ ☐	**15**	$18 \div 2 =$ ☐
6	$8 \div 2 =$ ☐	**16**	$50 \div 10 =$ ☐
7	$12 \div 2 =$ ☐	**17**	$40 \div 5 =$ ☐
8	$35 \div 5 =$ ☐	**18**	$6 \div 2 =$ ☐
9	$16 \div 2 =$ ☐	**19**	$60 \div 10 =$ ☐
10	$30 \div 10 =$ ☐	**20**	$50 \div 5 =$ ☐

Set D Date

1	$12 \div 3 =$ ☐	**11**	$60 \div 10 =$ ☐
2	$70 \div 10 =$ ☐	**12**	$8 \div 4 =$ ☐
3	$4 \div 4 =$ ☐	**13**	$3 \div 3 =$ ☐
4	$15 \div 3 =$ ☐	**14**	$90 \div 10 =$ ☐
5	$12 \div 4 =$ ☐	**15**	$16 \div 4 =$ ☐
6	$100 \div 10 =$ ☐	**16**	$80 \div 10 =$ ☐
7	$9 \div 3 =$ ☐	**17**	$5 \div 5 =$ ☐
8	$70 \div 10 =$ ☐	**18**	$20 \div 4 =$ ☐
9	$10 \div 10 =$ ☐	**19**	$25 \div 5 =$ ☐
10	$6 \div 3 =$ ☐	**20**	$50 \div 10 =$ ☐

Name _____

Set A   Date _____

1 14 + 6 = ☐   **11** 10 × 10 = ☐

2 5 × 5 = ☐   **12** 50 ÷ 10 = ☐

3 20 − 4 = ☐   **13** 9 + 9 = ☐

4 4 × 4 = ☐   **14** 6 ÷ 3 = ☐

5 13 + 4 = ☐   **15** 19 − 5 = ☐

6 10 ÷ 5 = ☐   **16** 70 ÷ 10 = ☐

7 19 − 6 = ☐   **17** 2 × 5 = ☐

8 15 + 4 = ☐   **18** 8 + 8 = ☐

9 35 ÷ 5 = ☐   **19** 20 − 8 = ☐

10 7 × 5 = ☐   **20** 45 ÷ 5 = ☐

Set B   Date _____

1 18 ÷ 2 = ☐   **11** 2 × 4 = ☐

2 7 + 7 = ☐   **12** 12 ÷ 2 = ☐

3 20 − 7 = ☐   **13** 8 + 9 = ☐

4 3 × 4 = ☐   **14** 15 ÷ 5 = ☐

5 6 × 5 = ☐   **15** 20 − 6 = ☐

6 6 + 6 = ☐   **16** 7 + 6 = ☐

7 19 − 4 = ☐   **17** 40 ÷ 10 = ☐

8 3 × 5 = ☐   **18** 8 × 5 = ☐

9 7 + 8 = ☐   **19** 9 + 6 = ☐

10 12 ÷ 4 = ☐   **20** 19 − 12 = ☐

Set C   Date _____

1 16 ÷ 4 = ☐   **11** 20 ÷ 5 = ☐

2 8 + 5 = ☐   **12** 3 × 3 = ☐

3 20 − 9 = ☐   **13** 8 + 7 = ☐

4 9 × 5 = ☐   **14** 19 − 13 = ☐

5 19 − 8 = ☐   **15** 9 ÷ 3 = ☐

6 7 + 9 = ☐   **16** 10 × 4 = ☐

7 30 ÷ 5 = ☐   **17** 16 + 3 = ☐

8 20 − 11 = ☐   **18** 16 ÷ 2 = ☐

9 50 ÷ 5 = ☐   **19** 2 × 3 = ☐

10 5 + 8 = ☐   **20** 15 + 3 = ☐

Set D   Date _____

1 40 ÷ 5 = ☐   **11** 6 × 10 = ☐

2 9 + 5 = ☐   **12** 8 + 6 = ☐

3 10 × 5 = ☐   **13** 4 × 5 = ☐

4 20 − 12 = ☐   **14** 25 ÷ 5 = ☐

5 12 ÷ 3 = ☐   **15** 20 − 13 = ☐

6 9 + 7 = ☐   **16** 5 + 9 = ☐

7 10 × 5 = ☐   **17** 19 − 7 = ☐

8 19 − 14 = ☐   **18** 20 ÷ 2 = ☐

9 6 + 8 = ☐   **19** 7 + 12 = ☐

10 14 ÷ 2 = ☐   **20** 100 ÷ 10 = ☐

Name _____

Set A   Date _____

1 14 + 6 =		**11** 7 + 9 =	
2 9 + 8 =		**12** 13 + 7 =	
3 8 + 11 =		**13** 16 + 4 =	
4 12 + 7 =		**14** 9 + 9 =	
5 6 + 12 =		**15** 6 + 14 =	
6 8 + 12 =		**16** 13 + 6 =	
7 9 + 7 =		**17** 7 + 13 =	
8 17 + 3 =		**18** 15 + 5 =	
9 8 + 9 =		**19** 12 + 8 =	
10 14 + 5 =		**20** 9 + 10 =	

Set B   Date _____

1 5 + 19 =		**11** 14 + 8 =	
2 18 + 5 =		**12** 7 + 17 =	
3 15 + 9 =		**13** 16 + 9 =	
4 18 + 7 =		**14** 13 + 9 =	
5 16 + 8 =		**15** 14 + 7 =	
6 6 + 18 =		**16** 15 + 8 =	
7 14 + 9 =		**17** 16 + 7 =	
8 15 + 6 =		**18** 17 + 8 =	
9 17 + 7 =		**19** 16 + 6 =	
10 19 + 6 =		**20** 15 + 7 =	

Set D   Date _____

1 20 − 9 =		**11** 19 − 11 =	
2 18 − 8 =		**12** 20 − 7 =	
3 19 − 6 =		**13** 18 − 9 =	
4 18 − 12 =		**14** 16 − 8 =	
5 20 − 10 =		**15** 19 − 9 =	
6 17 − 9 =		**16** 20 − 8 =	
7 19 − 12 =		**17** 18 − 10 =	
8 18 − 11 =		**18** 17 − 8 =	
9 19 − 7 =		**19** 19 − 8 =	
10 20 − 11 =		**20** 20 − 6 =	

Set D   Date _____

1 25 − 11 =		**11** 24 − 11 =	
2 23 − 6 =		**12** 25 − 16 =	
3 25 − 9 =		**13** 24 − 9 =	
4 24 − 7 =		**14** 23 − 7 =	
5 25 − 12 =		**15** 25 − 15 =	
6 24 − 8 =		**16** 24 − 16 =	
7 25 − 7 =		**17** 23 − 8 =	
8 24 − 15 =		**18** 25 − 13 =	
9 23 − 9 =		**19** 24 − 6 =	
10 25 − 14 =		**20** 25 − 8 =	

Name_____

Set A   Date_____

1 29 + 13 = ☐   11 24 + 19 = ☐

2 25 + 23 = ☐   12 28 + 18 = ☐

3 28 + 16 = ☐   13 24 + 16 = ☐

4 29 + 21 = ☐   14 29 + 17 = ☐

5 33 + 12 = ☐   15 28 + 22 = ☐

6 28 + 15 = ☐   16 25 + 18 = ☐

7 25 + 17 = ☐   17 24 + 17 = ☐

8 29 + 15 = ☐   18 28 + 17 = ☐

9 36 + 9 = ☐   19 29 + 18 = ☐

10 28 + 19 = ☐   20 25 + 19 = ☐

Set B   Date_____

1 38 + 47 = ☐   11 58 + 17 = ☐

2 42 + 58 = ☐   12 36 + 44 = ☐

3 65 + 17 = ☐   13 48 + 28 = ☐

4 43 + 48 = ☐   14 44 + 29 = ☐

5 77 + 15 = ☐   15 35 + 58 = ☐

6 39 + 36 = ☐   16 46 + 28 = ☐

7 66 + 25 = ☐   17 52 + 19 = ☐

8 45 + 37 = ☐   18 44 + 18 = ☐

9 78 + 17 = ☐   19 34 + 65 = ☐

10 37 + 36 = ☐   20 57 + 35 = ☐

Set C   Date_____

1 48 − 23 = ☐   11 38 − 19 = ☐

2 37 − 19 = ☐   12 46 − 17 = ☐

3 45 − 26 = ☐   13 50 − 27 = ☐

4 50 − 23 = ☐   14 48 − 17 = ☐

5 36 − 18 = ☐   15 35 − 18 = ☐

6 48 − 19 = ☐   16 50 − 37 = ☐

7 45 − 27 = ☐   17 49 − 28 = ☐

8 37 − 18 = ☐   18 43 − 26 = ☐

9 50 − 34 = ☐   19 48 − 29 = ☐

10 48 − 18 = ☐   20 50 − 25 = ☐

Set C   Date_____

1 77 − 26 = ☐   11 75 − 18 = ☐

2 69 − 34 = ☐   12 93 − 47 = ☐

3 83 − 41 = ☐   13 86 − 59 = ☐

4 97 − 62 = ☐   14 71 − 34 = ☐

5 64 − 19 = ☐   15 62 − 29 = ☐

6 73 − 18 = ☐   16 94 − 28 = ☐

7 92 − 24 = ☐   17 85 − 37 = ☐

8 86 − 37 = ☐   18 76 − 28 = ☐

9 58 − 19 = ☐   19 64 − 35 = ☐

10 62 − 33 = ☐   20 91 − 46 = ☐

Name _____

Set A   Date _____

1   $6 \times 4 =$ ☐   11 $9 \times 7 =$ ☐

2   $8 \times 6 =$ ☐   12 $7 \times 6 =$ ☐

3   $3 \times 8 =$ ☐   13 $8 \times 7 =$ ☐

4   $4 \times 7 =$ ☐   14 $9 \times 4 =$ ☐

5   $3 \times 6 =$ ☐   15 $8 \times 8 =$ ☐

6   $4 \times 8 =$ ☐   16 $3 \times 7 =$ ☐

7   $7 \times 4 =$ ☐   17 $8 \times 4 =$ ☐

8   $9 \times 6 =$ ☐   18 $4 \times 6 =$ ☐

9   $6 \times 6 =$ ☐   19 $7 \times 7 =$ ☐

10   $6 \times 7 =$ ☐   20 $6 \times 8 =$ ☐

Set B   Date _____

1   $8 \times 7 =$ ☐   11 $4 \times 7 =$ ☐

2   $3 \times 9 =$ ☐   12 $8 \times 9 =$ ☐

3   $6 \times 7 =$ ☐   13 $6 \times 4 =$ ☐

4   $7 \times 9 =$ ☐   14 $7 \times 8 =$ ☐

5   $8 \times 8 =$ ☐   15 $6 \times 9 =$ ☐

6   $4 \times 9 =$ ☐   16 $8 \times 3 =$ ☐

7   $7 \times 7 =$ ☐   17 $4 \times 8 =$ ☐

8   $6 \times 8 =$ ☐   18 $5 \times 9 =$ ☐

9   $5 \times 7 =$ ☐   19 $6 \times 6 =$ ☐

10   $9 \times 9 =$ ☐   20 $9 \times 8 =$ ☐

Set C   Date _____

1   $72 \div 9 =$ ☐   11 $45 \div 9 =$ ☐

2   $36 \div 4 =$ ☐   12 $24 \div 3 =$ ☐

3   $30 \div 6 =$ ☐   13 $32 \div 4 =$ ☐

4   $27 \div 3 =$ ☐   14 $60 \div 6 =$ ☐

5   $54 \div 6 =$ ☐   15 $54 \div 9 =$ ☐

6   $81 \div 9 =$ ☐   16 $24 \div 4 =$ ☐

7   $28 \div 4 =$ ☐   17 $48 \div 6 =$ ☐

8   $42 \div 6 =$ ☐   18 $21 \div 3 =$ ☐

9   $18 \div 3 =$ ☐   19 $20 \div 4 =$ ☐

10   $63 \div 9 =$ ☐   20 $36 \div 6 =$ ☐

Set D   Date _____

1   $21 \div 7 =$ ☐   11 $63 \div 7 =$ ☐

2   $48 \div 6 =$ ☐   12 $64 \div 8 =$ ☐

3   $72 \div 8 =$ ☐   13 $42 \div 7 =$ ☐

4   $36 \div 6 =$ ☐   14 $24 \div 8 =$ ☐

5   $35 \div 7 =$ ☐   15 $72 \div 9 =$ ☐

6   $81 \div 9 =$ ☐   16 $28 \div 7 =$ ☐

7   $56 \div 8 =$ ☐   17 $48 \div 8 =$ ☐

8   $49 \div 7 =$ ☐   18 $42 \div 6 =$ ☐

9   $63 \div 9 =$ ☐   19 $56 \div 7 =$ ☐

10   $32 \div 8 =$ ☐   20 $54 \div 9 =$ ☐

Name

Set A Date

1 43 – 16 =
2 25 + 17 =
3   4 × 9 =
4 63 ÷ 7 =
5 52 – 19 =
6 26 + 18 =
7   7 × 3 =
8 80 ÷ 10 =
9 45 + 39 =
10   9 × 5 =

11 35 ÷ 7 =
12 72 – 43 =
13 37 + 36 =
14   4 × 4 =
15 36 – 17 =
16 42 ÷ 7 =
17 61 – 18 =
18   5 × 5 =
19 28 + 18 =
20 24 ÷ 4 =

Set B Date

1 56 ÷ 7 =
2 61 – 27 =
3 18 ÷ 3 =
4   4 × 8 =
5 27 + 19 =
6 42 ÷ 6 =
7 53 – 37 =
8 48 ÷ 8 =
9 37 + 48 =
10   6 × 10 =

11 91 – 34 =
12 27 + 18 =
13   5 × 8 =
14 20 ÷ 4 =
15 42 – 18 =
16 49 ÷ 7 =
17   6 × 6 =
18 29 + 14 =
19 51 – 26 =
20   7 × 4 =

Set C Date

1 63 ÷ 7 =
2 48 – 39 =
3 26 + 15 =
4   6 × 4 =
5 47 – 28 =
6 36 ÷ 9 =
7 29 + 18 =
8   7 × 6 =
9 57 – 39 =
10 57 + 38 =

11 72 ÷ 9 =
12 49 + 38 =
13   8 × 3 =
14 82 – 38 =
15 64 ÷ 8 =
16 35 + 16 =
17 10 × 10 =
18 71 – 55 =
19   8 × 8 =
20 92 – 37 =

Set D Date

1 81 ÷ 9 =
2 55 – 27 =
3 36 + 18 =
4 72 ÷ 8 =
5   9 × 4 =
6 44 – 29 =
7 45 ÷ 9 =
8 37 + 19 =
9 32 ÷ 4 =
10 78 – 19 =

11 54 ÷ 9 =
12 47 + 24 =
13 52 – 27 =
14   7 × 7 =
15 38 + 18 =
16 10 × 9 =
17 53 – 28 =
18 63 ÷ 9 =
19 45 + 29 =
20 81 – 43 =

For the first group of questions you will have five seconds to work out each answer and write it down.

1 Add together 6, 7 and 4.
2 Write the number that is 5 less than 200.
3 What is 336 to the nearest hundred?
4 What is 8 multiplied by 5?
5 How many days are there in January?
6 What is a shape with five sides called?
7 How many millimetres in 3 centimetres?
8 What is half of 16?

For the next group of questions you will have ten seconds to work out each answer and write it down.

9 Add 46 and 27.
10 There are three digits on your sheet. What is the largest number you can write using those digits?
11 Two-fifths of the class are girls. What fraction are boys?
12 If you turn one right angle clockwise from north, which direction are you facing?
13 How many minutes from 9:30 to 10:15?
14 What is the cost of nine books at £5 each?

15 What is the change from £1 if I spend 38 pence?
16 How many millilitres in half a litre?
17 Look at the angle on your sheet. Is it bigger or smaller than a right angle.
18 What is the remainder when 27 is divided by 5?
19 How many grams are there in 4 kilograms?
20 Look at the shape on your sheet. Draw a line of symmetry on the shape.

For the next group of questions you will have fifteen seconds to work out each answer and write it down.

21 Look at the numbers on your sheet. Put a ring round each of the odd numbers.
22 How much change do I get from £5 if I spend £2 and 25 pence?
23 The temperature is 3 degrees Celsius. What will it be after a fall of 5 degrees Celsius?
24 A number has 6 added to it to make 13. What was the number?
25 There are 48 people at a party. Twenty-seven more arrive. How many are there altogether?

Name _____

Date _____

Total marks ☐

Time: 5 seconds

1 ☐

2 ☐

3 ☐

4 ☐

5 ☐ days

6 ☐

7 ☐ mm

8 ☐

Time: 10 seconds

9 ☐

10 ☐ 6, 9, 4

11 ☐

12 ☐ north

13 ☐ minutes

14 £ ☐

15 ☐ 38p

16 ☐ ml

17
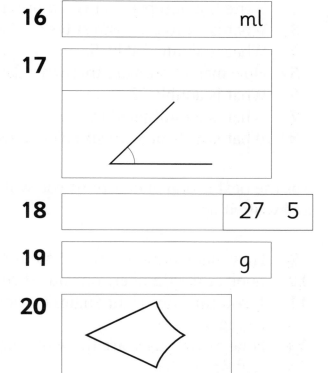

18 ☐ 27 | 5

19 ☐ g

20 ☐

Time: 15 seconds

21 6 11 15 18 23

22 £ ☐

23 ☐ °C

24 ☐

25 ☐

For the first group of questions you will have five seconds to work out each answer and write it down.

1 Subtract 7 from 15.
2 Write the number that is 3 more than 198.
3 What is 74 to the nearest ten?
4 What is 45 divided by 5?
5 How many hours are there in a day?
6 What is double 7?
7 What is 9 multiplied by 10?
8 What is a shape with six sides called?

For the next group of questions you will have ten seconds to work out each answer and write it down.

9 How many minutes from 2:45 to 3:10?
10 Look at the numbers on your sheet. Put a ring round the smallest one.
11 If you turn two right angles clockwise from west, which direction are you facing?
12 How many halves are there in four whole ones?
13 Add 68 and 29.
14 What is the remainder when 74 is divided by 10?

15 How many grams are there in half a kilogram?
16 Look at at the shape on your sheet. Mark the right angles with a cross.
17 Look at the shape on your sheet. What is it called?
18 What is the cost of five toys at £7 each?
19 What is the change from £1 if I spend 62 pence?
20 How many millilitres in 3 litres?

For the next group of questions you will have fifteen seconds to work out each answer and write it down.

21 Look at the numbers on your sheet. Put a ring round each of the even numbers.
22 What number divided by 3 gives 4 remainder 2?
23 A train leaves the station at 8:30 am and travels for $2\frac{1}{2}$ hours. At what time does it stop?
24 Subtract 39 from 84.
25 How much change do I get from £10 if I spend £5 and 36 pence?

Time: 5 seconds

1 [ ]

2 [ ]

3 [ ]

4 [ ]

5 [hours]

6 [ ]

7 [ ]

8 [·]

16

17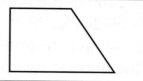

18 [£]

19 [£]

20 [ml]

Time: 10 seconds

9 [mins]

10 [25   2·5   2   52]

11 [west]

12 [halves]

13 [ ]

14 [ ]

15 [g]

Time: 15 seconds

21 [8   12   15   19   26]

22 [ ]

23 [8:30   2½ hours]

24 [ ]

25 [£]

For the first group of questions you will have five seconds to work out the answer and write it down.

1   Multiply 75 by 10.
2   What is 2460 to the nearest hundred?
3   What is 56 divided by 8?
4   Write a half as a decimal.
5   Write the number two thousand and ten in figures.
6   Change $6\frac{1}{2}$ kilograms into grams.
7   What is 9 multiplied by 6?
8   Write quarter to nine as it would appear on a digital watch.

For the next group of questions you will have ten seconds to work out the answer and write it down.

9   The side of a square is 5 centimetres. What is the area of the square?
10   I take 3 hours and 40 minutes to travel home from my holiday. I set out at nine thirty. At what time do I get home?
11   Look at the numbers on your sheet. What is the mode of the numbers?
12   What temperature is 4 degrees Celsius warmer than −1 degree Celsius?
13   What is 5·6 multiplied by 100?
14   What is 25 per cent of £200?
15   On your sheet is a scale. Estimate the number shown by the arrow.
16   Look at the shape on your sheet. What is it called?
17   Subtract 75 from 232.
18   How many nines in 720?
19   What is the volume of the cuboid on your sheet?
20   Jack saves £1.20 a week. How much will he have saved in seven weeks?

For the next group of questions you will have fifteen seconds to work out the answer and write it down.

21   Look at the numbers on your sheet. Draw a ring round each number that is a multiple of 3.
22   Start with 4. Multiply it by 7 and add 2. What is the answer?
23   Approximately, what is the answer when you add 327 to 412?
24   In a class of 25 children, 40 per cent are girls. How many girls is that?
25   What shape has four triangular faces and one square face?

Name

Date

Total marks

Time: 5 seconds

1

2

3

4

5

6   g

7

8

Time: 10 seconds

9   cm^2

10

3 h 40 min   9:30

11

3, 4, 3, 7, 4, 3

12   °C

13

14 £

15

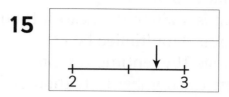

16

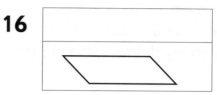

17

18

19   cm^3

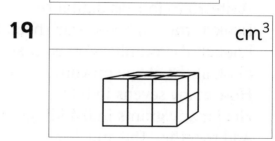

20 £

Time: 15 seconds

21 9 16 24 38 45

22

23

24

25

For the first group of questions you will have five seconds to work out the answer and write it down.

1   Divide 320 by 10.
2   What is 4 480 to the nearest thousand?
3   What is 9 multiplied by 7?
4   Change 10½ centimetres into millimetres.
5   Write the number forty thousand and four in figures.
6   Add together 15, 8 and 13.
7   What is 64 divided by 8?
8   How many degrees in a right angle?

For the next group of questions you will have ten seconds to work out the answer and write it down.

9   The side of a square is 9 centimetres. What is the perimeter of the square?
10   Write 25 to four as digital time.
11   Look at the angle on your sheet. Estimate the size of the angle in degrees.
12   Look at the numbers on your sheet. Put a ring round the median.
13   Look at the shape on your sheet. Is it an isosceles triangle?
14   How many sevens in 630?
15   How many grams in 0·4 kilograms?
16   Add together 156 and 247.
17   What is 32·9 divided by 100?
18   What is 50 per cent of 72?
19   How many 200-millilitre glasses can be filled from a 2-litre bottle?
20   Change 3¼ hours to minutes.

For the next group of questions you will have fifteen seconds to work out the answer and write it down.

21   Look at the numbers on your sheet. Put a ring round each one that is a factor of 24.
22   Billy has to walk 1·5 kilometres home from school. When he has walked 700 metres how much further has he to walk?
23   When an amount of money is shared between six people they have £4.30 each. What was the amount of money?
24   The sides of a rectangle are 4·5 centimetres and 5 centimetres. What is its perimeter?
25   What is three-fifths of 60?

Time: 5 seconds

1 [ ]

2 [ ]

3 [ ]

4 [mm]

5 [ ]

6 [ ]

7 [ ]

8 [ ]

13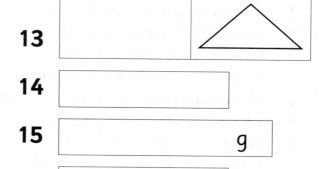

14 [ ]

15 [g]

16 [ ]

17 [ ]

18 [ ]

19 [ ]

20 [min]

Time: 10 seconds

9 [cm]

10 [ ]

11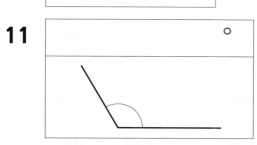

12 [5, 5, 5, 6, 6, 8, 10]

Time: 15 seconds

21 [8 1 14 6 5]

22 [m]
[1·5 km   700 m]

23 [£]

24 [cm]
[4·5 cm   5 cm]

25 [ ]

143

For the first group of questions you will have five seconds to work out the answer and write it down.

1 A number multiplied by 4 is 36. What is the number?

2 What is 2 460 divided by 10?

3 What is 108 divided by 9?

4 Write 25 per cent as a fraction.

5 How many degrees in two right angles?

6 Change 4 080 metres into kilometres.

7 What is 8 multiplied by 30?

8 Write 2:00 pm as 24-hour time.

For the next group of questions you will have ten seconds to work out the answer and write it down.

9 The side of an equilateral triangle is 4 centimetres. What is the perimeter of the triangle?

10 A train arrives at 13:58. It is 12 minutes early. At what time should it have arrived?

11 Look at the numbers on your sheet. What is the mean of the numbers?

12 What is the change in temperature from –5 degrees Celsius to 3 degrees Celsius?

13 What is 1·7 subtracted from 2·1?

14 What is 20 per cent of £120?

15 On your sheet is a scale. Put an arrow on it to show the probability of picking an odd number from the numbers one to 10.

16 Look at the shape on your sheet. What order of rotational symmetry does it have?

17 Subtract 426 from 634.

18 How many fourteens in 280?

19 Twenty-five per cent of a number is 60. What is the number?

20 Look at the angle on your sheet. Estimate the size of the angle in degrees.

For the next group of questions you will have fifteen seconds to work out the answer and write it down.

21 Look at the numbers on your sheet. Draw a ring round each one that is a square number.

22 I think of a number, multiply it by 2 and add 6 to get 20. What was the number?

23 The numbers on your sheet show the number of people in the audience at a play on three nights. How many people went to see the play?

24 The mean of five numbers is 10. Four of the numbers are shown on your sheet. What is the fifth number?

25 How many edges does a triangular prism have?

Time: 5 seconds

1 ☐

2 ☐

3 ☐

4 ☐

5 ☐ °

6 ☐ km

7 ☐

8 ☐

Time: 10 seconds

9 ☐ cm

10
☐
| 13:58 | 12 |

11 ☐ | 17 13 12 18

12 ☐ °C

13 ☐

14 £ ☐

15  0 ——————————— 1

16 ☐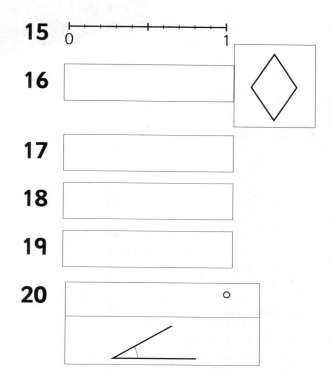

17 ☐

18 ☐

19 ☐

20
☐ °

Time: 15 seconds

21 | 81 64 56 9 30 |

22 ☐ | ×2 +6 |

23
☐
| 217   300   489 |

24
☐
| 7   15   6   9 |

25 ☐ edges

Answers

C1 Place value
1 480
2 592
3 330
4 650
5 220
6 731
7 770
8 600
9 841
10 160

C2 Place value
Round to 300:
290, 274, 348, 342
Round to 400: 359
Round to 500:
452, 460, 471, 481,
540
Round to 600:
559, 603, 639, 641

C3 Place value
< 20 = {99, 101}
> 120, < 210 = {194}
< 210, < 330 = {220,
     290, 301}
> 330, < 550 = {352,
     402}
> 550, < 700 = {570,
     600, 652}
> 700, < 910 {701,
     750, 799}

C4 Place value
1 <
2 <
3 =
4 <
5 =
6 <
7 >
8 <
9 >
10 >
11 <
12 >
13 >
14 =

15 <
16 <
17 <
18 =
19 >
20 >

C5 Place value
Set A 1 76
2 510
3 41
4 630
5 14
6 3 200
7 320
8 89 000
9 81
10 92 400
Set B 1 3·4
2 62
3 43·6
4 94
5 1·3
6 40
7 5·6
8 50
9 0·057
10 734

C6 Place value
27→270,
34→340,
681→6 810,
608→6 080,
43→430,
123→1 230,
151→1 510,
501→5 010

C7 Place value
1 27
2 416
3 37·4
4 6·3
5 34
6 739
7 47·9
8 8·2
1 2 400

2 3 900
3 13 800
4 92 100
5 600
6 4 100
7 34 800
8 704 200

C8 Place value
1 × 10
2 × 100
3 ÷ 10
4 ÷ 10
5 × 100
6 ÷ 100
7 × 10
8 ÷ 100
9 ÷ 100
10 × 100

C9 Place value
1 30→402
2 500→26
3 90→702
4 800→51
5 3→640
6 400→1 062
7 7 000→339
8 200→9 018
9 4 000→70 392
10 60 000→2 134

C10 Place value
1 100
2 999
3 102
4 987
5 1 111
6 9 999
7 1 023
8 11 111
9 98 765
10 10 234

C11 Addition
Sums ringed are:
17 + 3, 14 + 6,
19 + 1, 4 + 16,
20 + 0, 10 + 10,

8 + 12, 2 + 18,
13 + 7, 9 + 11,
1 + 19, 16 + 4,
10 + 10, 11 + 9,
12 + 8, 7 + 13, 15 + 5

C12 Addition
Column 1
27 + 73, 48 + 52,
72 + 28, 68 + 32,
77 + 23, 36 + 64
Column 2
54 + 46, 26 + 74,
49 + 51, 16 + 84,
39 + 61, 88 + 12

C13 Addition
Set A 1 57
2 81
3 88
4 59
5 36
6 72
7 85
8 54
9 62
10 46
Set B 1 78
2 73
3 32
4 69
5 85
6 84
7 52
8 61
9 89
10 37

C14 Addition
1 40
2 70
3 40
4 70
5 20
6 90
7 100
8 60
9 90
10 100

146

C15 Addition
Variety of answers possible

C16 Addition
Answers for second option
Set A 1 52
2 83
3 87
4 56
5 64
6 68
7 81
8 90
9 85
10 77
Set B 1 41
2 76
3 91
4 63
5 78
6 64
7 96
8 97
9 72
10 78

C17 Addition
Set A 1 37
2 67
3 57
4 97
5 27
6 77
Set B 1 72
2 42
3 92
4 82
5 62
6 32
Set C 1 93
2 63
3 33
4 53
5 83
6 43
Set D 1 55
2 95
3 65
4 85
5 35
6 75

C18 Addition
1 5, 90, 95
2 14, 70, 84
3 11, 80, 91
4 10, 80, 90
5 11, 50, 61
6 13, 50, 63
7 10, 90, 100
8 11, 70, 81
9 16, 60, 76
10 9, 60, 69

C19 Addition
1 85
2 65
3 21, 71
4 40, 23, 63
5 50, 45, 95
6 30, 25, 55
7 40, 45, 85
8 60, 32, 92
9 70, 25, 95
10 50, 33, 83

C20 Addition
1 $30 + 60 = 90$
2 $50 + 30 = 80$
3 $40 + 30 = 70$
4 $30 + 60 = 90$
5 $100 + 500 = 600$
6 $400 + 500 = 900$
7 $400 + 300 = 700$
8 $400 + 400 = 800$

C21 Subtraction
Set A 1 14
2 7
3 12
4 10
5 13
Set B 1 12
2 5
3 10
4 3
5 8
Set C 1 8
2 13
3 10
4 14
5 7
Set D 1 13
2 7
3 11
4 14
5 16

C22 Subtraction
1 4
2 9
3 3
4 80, 8
5 60, 7
6 90, 2
7 70, 6
8 80, 1
9 60, 4
10 70, 5

C23 Subtraction
1 73
2 58
3 64
4 39
5 27
6 25
7 44
8 49
9 35

10 28

C24 Subtraction
Set A 1 63
2 42
3 29
4 51
5 19
6 54
7 45
8 37
9 58
10 26
Set B 1 57
2 45
3 60
4 71
5 26
6 32
7 49
8 64
9 28
10 53

C25 Subtraction
Set A 1 3
2 8
3 4
4 2
5 5
6 2
7 3
8 2
9 1
10 3
Set B 1 6
2 6
3 5
4 3
5 1
6 1
7 8
8 7
9 5
10 6

C26 Subtraction
Bingo game

C27 Subtraction
Ring the sums:
27 – 11, 71–55,
39 – 23, 45 – 29,
64 – 48, 53 – 37,
97 – 81, 91 – 75

C28 Subtraction
1 8
2 19
3 40, 25
4 50, 24
5 30, 27
6 48, 20, 28
7 66, 30, 36
8 75, 40, 35
9 93, 60, 33

10 82, 50, 32

C29 Subtraction
1 37
2 27, 27, 46
3 32, 32, 58
4 38, 38, 72
5 28, 28, 83
6 23
7 82, 82
8 42, 42, 18
9 43, 43, 26
10 82, 82, 53

C30 Subtraction
1 55
2 14
3 46
4 15
5 58 km
6 29

C31 Multiplication
Set A 1 8
2 12
3 18
4 6
5 14
Set B 1 10
2 50
3 20
4 40
5 25
Set C 1 100
2 80
3 50
4 30
5 60
Set D 1 20
2 8
3 4
4 14
5 18

C32 Multiplication
A 5, 10, 15, 20, 35
B 6, 9, 15
C 10, 70, 90
D 4, 12, 16, 20

C33 Multiplication
$\times 2 \rightarrow$ 2, 10, 16, 22, 6, 24, 12, 0, 20, 14, 4, 8, 18
$\times 5 \rightarrow$ 5, 25, 40, 55, 15, 60, 30, 0, 50, 35, 10, 20, 45
$\times 10 \rightarrow$ 10, 50, 80, 110, 30, 120, 60, 0, 100, 70, 20, 40, 90

C34 Multiplication
1 12
2 20
3 35

4	16	
5	60	
6	100	
7	30	
8	8	
9	40	
10	60	

C35 Multiplication
Set A	**1**	12
	2	27
	3	18
	4	24
Set B	**1**	30
	2	60
	3	42
	4	18
Set C	**1**	8
	2	36
	3	28
	4	20
Set D	**1**	54
	2	72
	3	27
	4	90

C36 Multiplication
No answers
Timed grid

C37 Multiplication
$4 \times \rightarrow 26, 34$
$6 \times \rightarrow 32, 52$
$8 \times \rightarrow 28, 34, 54$
$3 \times \rightarrow 25, 32, 49$
$9 \times \rightarrow 34, 56, 78$
$7 \times \rightarrow 32, 54$

C38 Multiplication
1	8
2	6
3	54
4	10
5	8
6	21
7	9
8	7
9	100
10	7

C39 Multiplication
Set A	48, 48, 48, 48
Set B	$36, 36, 36 \div 4,$ $36 \div 9$
Set C	$56, 7 \times 8 = 56,$ $56 \div 7 = 8,$ $56 \div 8 = 7$
Set D	$42, 6 \times 7 = 42,$ $42 \div 6 = 7,$ $42 \div 7 = 6$

C40 Multiplication
1	12
2	120
3	1200
4	120

5	35
6	350
7	3500
8	350
1	160
2	300
3	360
4	560
5	210
6	3600
7	3200
8	2700
9	2500
10	4200

C41 Division
Set A	**1**	yes
	2	no
	3	no
	4	no
	5	yes
	6	yes
	7	yes
	8	yes
	9	no
	10	no
Set B	**1**	no
	2	no
	3	yes
	4	yes
	5	yes
	6	no
	7	yes
	8	yes
	9	no
	10	yes

C42 Division

C43 Division
1	10
2	3
3	4
4	7
5	9
6	4
7	4
8	8
9	9 r1
10	9 (r0)
11	3 r1
12	3 r1
13	8 r1
14	5 r3

C44 Division
1	4

2	5
3	6
4	10p
5	4
6	3
7	3, 3
8	4, 3

C45 Division
Set A	*Divisible by 6:* 36, 42, 48, 54
	Divisible by 7: 35, 56, 49
Set B	*Divisible by 8:* 32, 40, 48, 56, 72
	Divisible by 6: 36, 42, 48, 72
Set C	*Divisible by 9:* 36, 45, 54, 63
	Divisible by 7: 28, 56, 63, 70
Set D	*Divisible by 8:* 48, 64, 72, 80
	Divisible by 9: 45, 54, 72, 81

C46 Division
Circled numbers:
13, 19, 25, 31, 37, 43, 49, 55
Square around numbers: 10, 18, 26, 34, 42, 50, 58

C47 Division

C48 Division
Set A	**1**	9
	2	90
	3	900
	4	90
	5	6
	6	60
	7	600
	8	60
Set B	**1**	50
	2	90
	3	600
	4	600
	5	80
	6	40
	7	90
	8	70
	9	7
	10	70

C49 Division
1	$7, 7 \times 8 = 56$
2	$9, 9 \times 9 = 81$
3	$7, 7 \times 7 = 49$
4	$9, 9 \times 8 = 72$
5	$9, 9 \times 4 = 36$
6	$6, 6 \times 7 = 42$

C50 Division
1	8
2	4
3	7
4	3
5	7
6	6
7	9
8	6
9	8
10	5
11	8
12	6
13	6
14	7
15	8
16	9
17	8
18	7
19	3
20	9

C51 Number patterns
1	✔
2	✘
3	✔
4	✔
5	✘
6	✔
7	✘
8	✘
9	✔
10	✔
11	✘
12	✔
13	✔
14	✘
15	✔
16	✔

C52 Number patterns
1	10, 12
2	13, 16, +3
3	9, 7, −2
4	6, 3, −3
5	11, 13, +2
6	14, 17, +3
7	10, 7, −3
8	17, 21, +4

C53 Number patterns
Set A	11, 14, 7, 12
Set B	7, 9, 14, 12
Set C	7, 4, 9, 5
Set D	9, 4, 7, 11

C54 Number patterns
Variety of answers possible

C55 Number patterns
$12 \rightarrow 2 \times 6, 3 \times 4$
$18 \rightarrow 1 \times 18, 2 \times 9,$
$\quad 3 \times 6$
$20 \rightarrow 1 \times 20, 2 \times 10,$
$\quad 4 \times 5$
$32 \rightarrow 1 \times 32, 2 \times 16,$
$\quad 4 \times 8$
$24 \rightarrow 1 \times 24, 2 \times 12,$
$\quad 3 \times 8, 4 \times 6$
$40 \rightarrow 1 \times 40, 2 \times 20,$
$\quad 4 \times 10, 5 \times 8$

C56 Number patterns
Variety of answers possible

C57 Number patterns
1 8, +4
2 8, ×2
3 9, ×2 +1
4 11, ×3 −1

C58 Number patterns
1 25, 36, add odd numbers *(square numbers)*
2 11, 16, add one more
3 4, 2, divide by two
4 31, 63, difference is doubling
5 31, 46, difference goes up in threes

C59 Number patterns
Set A ×2, 8, 12, 6, 14
Set B ×3, 15, 6, 24, 12
Set C ×3, −2, 22, 7, 16
Set D −2, ×4, 12, 28, 16

C60 Number patterns
1 4
2 7
3 8
4 8
5 6

C61 Fractions
Variety of answers possible

C62 Fractions
1 2
2 $\frac{1}{6} + \frac{1}{6} + \frac{1}{6} = \frac{3}{6}$
3 $\frac{1}{8} + \frac{1}{8} + \frac{1}{8} = \frac{3}{8}$
4 $\frac{1}{10} + \frac{1}{10} + \frac{1}{10} = \frac{3}{10}$
5 $\frac{1}{4} + \frac{1}{4} + \frac{1}{4} = \frac{3}{4}$
6 $\frac{1}{3} + \frac{1}{3} = \frac{2}{3}$

C63 Fractions
Variety of answers possible

C64 Fractions
$\frac{1}{4}$, 4
tenth, 10
fifth, $\frac{1}{5}$
$\frac{1}{3}$, 3
sixth, 6
$\frac{1}{8}$, 8
ninth, $\frac{1}{9}$

C65 Fractions
1 5
2 5
3 4
4 4
5 2
6 6
7 6
8 10
9 6
10 8
11 18
12 15
13 21
14 40
15 24
16 63

C66 Fractions
1 14
2 24
3 25
4 21
5 40
6 9
7 20
8 50

C67 Fractions
Set A $\frac{1}{3}$, <, <, >, >
Set B $\frac{7}{10}$, >, >, >, <
Set C $\frac{2}{3}$, >, >, <, >
Set D $\frac{1}{4}$, <, <, <, <

C68 Fractions
$\frac{1}{2} \rightarrow \frac{2}{4} = \frac{3}{6} = \frac{4}{8} = \frac{5}{10}$
$\frac{1}{4} \rightarrow \frac{2}{8} = \frac{3}{12} = \frac{4}{16}$
$\frac{1}{3} \rightarrow \frac{2}{6} = \frac{3}{9}$
$\frac{1}{5} \rightarrow \frac{2}{10} = \frac{3}{15} = \frac{4}{20}$

C69 Fractions
Shading of:
1 $\frac{3}{6}$
2 $\frac{2}{8}$
3 $\frac{2}{20}$
4 $\frac{4}{12}$
5 $\frac{3}{15}$
6 $\frac{6}{9}$

C70 Fractions
1 12
2 4
3 2
4 4
5 30
6 20
7 6

8 40

C71 Decimals
Numbers plotted on lines

C72 Decimals
1 1
2 2
3 4
4 8
5 7
6 5
7 4
8 6
9 9
10 10

C73 Decimals
Set A 1 2·3
2 4·7
3 5·9
4 1·5
5 3·6
6 8·0
7 4·1
8 8·2
9 3·0
10 10·0
Set B 1 5·2
2 6·6
3 4·7
4 3·8
5 9·3
6 6·9
7 4·9
8 3·0
9 9·9
10 2·0

C74 Decimals
Add to 8: 2·6 + 5·4, 3·5 + 4·5, 3·3 + 4·7, 2·5 + 5·5, 1·8 + 6·2
Difference of 0·4: 2·6 − 2·2, 6·2 − 5·8, 4·9 − 4·5, 3·8 − 3·4, 2·3 − 1·9

C75 Decimals
Numbers plotted on lines

C76 Decimals
1 2·3, 3·4, 4·3
2 2·5, 5·0, 5·2
3 4·0, 4·3, 4·7
4 6·0, 6·9, 7·0
5 0·25, 0·39, 0·52
6 1·1, 1·17, 1·70
7 5·29, 5·3, 5·39
8 1·14, 1·41, 14·1
9 6·1, 6·12, 6·2
10 7·49, 7·5, 7·51

C77 Decimals
1 3·6, 4·6
2 7·8, 8·8
3 8·3, 9·3
4 6·5, 7·5
5 2·7, 3·7
6 5·9, 6·9
7 7·0, 8·0
8 4·51, 5·51
9 5·44, 6·44
10 3·32, 4·32

C78 Decimals
1 2·7
2 420
3 3 600
4 5·13
5 0·17
6 34·3
7 2 620
8 0·09
9 570
10 0·83

C79 Decimals
1 80
2 142
3 8·6
4 1·1
5 8·0
6 6·8

C80 Decimals
Squares: 3·52, 4·5, 1·51, 8·52, 7·51
Circles: 4·35, 2·45, 9·15, 3·05, 6·35

C81 Money
1 £4
2 £3.50
3 £5.60
4 £8.24
5 £7.20
6 £6.03
7 £0.94
8 £0.50
9 £0.06
10 £0.12
11 525
12 730
13 126
14 340
15 407
16 300
17 28
18 7
19 60
20 600

C82 Money
Other combinations are possible
1 2, 1
2 5, 1
3 2, 1

4	2, 4
5	6, 3
6	7, 0, 4, 0
7	8, 0, 1, 1
8	9, 1, 2, 0

C83 Money

Set A
1	£1.30
2	£3.50
3	£6.90
4	£8.00
5	£4.73
6	£9.02
7	£6.08
8	£1.14
9	£6.18
10	£1.09

Set B
1	£4.30
2	£6.50
3	£3.70
4	£4.90
5	£7.03
6	£7.94
7	£8.83
8	£1.88
9	£0.44
10	£0.81

C84 Money

1	36p
2	71p
3	48p, 52p
4	90p, 10p
5	35p, 65p
6	50p
7	£1.80
8	£2.20

C85 Money

Set A
1	£1.80
2	£3.60
3	£6.48
4	£6.54
5	£9.33
6	£12.68
7	£16.42
8	£18.38
9	£4.49
10	£8.44

Set B
1	£1.70
2	£6.60
3	£3.91
4	£2.47
5	£12.24
6	£4.37
7	£7.43
8	£3.32
9	£8.42
10	£14.51

C86 Money

Set A
1	£6.30
2	£2.35
3	£5.05
4	£6.55
5	£6.44

6	£4.33
7	£2.69
8	£2.46
9	£7.38
10	£3.87

Set B
1	£5.75
2	£5.00
3	£7.50
4	£3.80
5	£6.64
6	£4.99
7	£3.86
8	£5.53
9	£7.42
10	£4.81

C87 Money

1	10 weeks
2	7 weeks
3	13 weeks
4	18 weeks
5	7 weeks
6	6 weeks
7	10 weeks
8	13 weeks

C88 Money

1	£11.96
2	£41.94
3	£14.97
4	£13.86
5	£19.90
6	£6.98
7	£10.98
8	£8.97
9	£12.96
10	£12.96

C89 Money

1	£4.14
2	£3.96
3	£24.90
4	£15.85
5	£5.54
6	£19.54

C90 Money

Game Sheet

C91 Time

1	Clock showing 3:30
2	Twenty past four
3	7:15 Quarter past seven
4	9:15
5	5 to 2

C92 Time

1	July
2	May
3	September
4	January
5	June
6	July
7	July

8	September
9	May
10	March

C93 Time

1	1h 15 mins
2	3h
3	2h 10 mins
4	45 mins
5	1h 15 mins
6	20 mins
7	2h 10 mins
8	50 mins
9	1h 5 mins
10	1h 5 mins

C94 Time

Set A
1	4:00
2	4:30
3	8:00
4	10:30
5	7:00
6	3:00
7	8:45
8	2:00
9	5:45
10	3:30

Set B
1	7:15
2	4:45
3	6:30
4	11:30
5	9:45
6	9:00
7	3:00
8	1:30
9	11:00
10	3:30

C95 Time

1	3:20 am 03:20
2	1:15 pm 13:15
3	4:50 am 04:50
4	7:35 pm 19:35
5	11:05 pm 23:05

C96 Time

1	1h 5 mins
2	1h 30 mins
3	1h 50 mins
4	2h 5 mins
5	3h 0 mins
6	80 mins
7	105 mins
8	135 mins
9	155 mins
10	200 mins

C97 Time

1	A
2	C
3	21 mins
4	C
5	1h 49 mins

C98 Time

Set A
1	3:00

2	5:05
3	7:55
4	6:25
5	8:50
6	10:20
7	11:10
8	11:57
9	10:30
10	7:35

Set B
1	4:45
2	6:50
3	7:55
4	8:30
5	10:35
6	12:40
7	6:15
8	4:10
9	2:00
10	3:05

C99 Time

1	3h 5 mins
2	3h 15 mins
3	45 mins
4	2h 45 mins
5	1h 50 mins
6	4h 5 mins
7	1h 45 mins
8	2h 55 mins
9	3h 45 mins
10	2h 50 mins

C100 Time

1	10:15, 10:30
2	07:35, 08:00, *Add 25 minutes*
3	18:35, 19:05, *Add 30 minutes*
4	19:55, 20:10, *Add 15 minutes*
5	00:05, 00:30, *Add 25 minutes*
6	12:45, 13:05, *Add 20 minutes*

C101 Angles

Right angles: c, f
Less than: a, e, g, i
More than: b, d, h

C102 Angles

Marking angles

C103 Angles

1	2
2	1
3	3
4	2
5	1
6	1
7	3
8	2
9	West
10	South

C104 Angles
1. e
2. a
3. g
4. b
5. c
6. g
7. d
8. h

C105 Angles
Marking angles

C106 Angles
1. ✔
2. ✘ West
3. ✔

C107 Angles
Allow + or − 10°
1. 50°
2. 30°
3. 120°
4. 40°
5. 100°
6. 140°
7. 130°
8. 80°

C108 Angles
a = 50°
b = 120°
c = 50°
d = 130°
e = 25°
f = 135°
g = 60°

C109 Shape

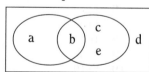

C110 Shape
1. T
2. T
3. F
4. T
5. F
6. T
7. T
8. T
9. T
10. F

C111 Shape
1. Parallelogram
2. Hexagon
3. Isosceles triangle or trapezium
4. Kite

C112 Shape
Properties will vary
1. Cone
2. Triangular prism
3. Square based pyramid
4. Cylinder
5. Cuboid
6. Tetrahedron, triangular based pyramid

C113 Area and Perimeter
1. 8 cm²
2. 4 cm²
3. 10 cm²
4. 10 cm²
5. 11.5 cm²
6. 9 cm²
7. 16 cm
8. 16 cm

C114 Area and Perimeter
1. 16 cm²
2. 3, 5, or 1, 15
3. 24 m
4. 48 m², 28 m
5. 400 m
6. 36 cm

C115 Volume and Capacity
1. 250 ml, 50 ml, 90 ml
2. 500 ml (±100), 250 ml (±50), 500 ml (±100)
3. (Shading 750 ml)

C116 Volume and Capacity
1. 1 000 ml
2. 1 500 ml
3. 400 ml
4. No
5. 5
6. 10

C117 Volume and Capacity
1. 12 cm³
2. 9 cm³
3. 36 cm³
4. 75 cm³
5. 48 cm³
6. 120

C118 Volume and Capacity
1. 1, 3, 4
2. 2, 3, 3
3. 2, 2, 5
4. 2, 3, 4
5. 2, 2, 8

C119 Length
Allow + or − 1cm
1. 5 cm
2. 7 cm
3. 12 cm
4. 4 cm
5. 9 cm
6. 14 cm
7. 3 m
8. 2 m

C120 Length
1. 10 mm
2. 2 km
3. 1 km
4. 15 cm
5. 300 cm
6. 150 cm

C121 Length
200 cm = 2 m
2 000 m = 2 km
35 mm = 3.5 cm
350 cm = $3\frac{1}{2}$ m
3 500 m = 3.5 km

C122 Length
1. T
2. F
3. T
4. 50 cm
5. 70 cm
6. 1200 m
7. 6
8. 3 600 m

C123 Weight
1. 500 g
2. 150 g
3. 100 g
4. 5 kg
5. 25 kg
6. 50 g
7. 25 g
8. 300 g
9. 3 kg
10. 70 kg

C124 Weight
1. 5
2. 59 kg
3. 500 g
4. 4 000 g
5. 250 g
6. 3.5 kg or 3 500 g

C125 Weight
1. 1 000 g
2. 4 000 g
3. 6 kg
4. 3 500 g
5. 2 250 g
6. 2
7. 6 or 7
8. 4

C126 Weight
2kg: 1 400 g + 0.60 kg, 1 250 g + 0.75 kg, 1.50 kg + 500 g, 1 750 g + 250 g, 1.20 kg + 800 g
200g: 1.20 kg − 1 000 g, 2 kg − 1.80 kg, 1.56 kg − 1 360 g, 5 100 g − 4.90 kg, 6.10 kg − 5.90 kg

C127 Handling Data
1. 4
2. 21
3. B
4. 14
5. ✔
6. ✘
7. ✔
8. ✔
9. 4, 5

C128 Handling Data
1. 5
2. 3
3. 4
4. 5
5. 6
6. 1
7. 4
8. 17

C129 Handling Data
Plotting points:
A at 0.5, B at 0.1, C at 0, D at 0.4, E at 0.3, F at 0.7

C130 Handling Data
1. $\frac{3}{6}$ or $\frac{1}{2}$
2. $\frac{1}{6}$
3. $\frac{3}{6}$ or $\frac{1}{2}$
4. $\frac{2}{6}$ or $\frac{1}{3}$
5. $\frac{5}{6}$
6. $\frac{4}{8}$ or $\frac{1}{2}$
7. $\frac{3}{8}$
8. $\frac{2}{8}$ or $\frac{1}{4}$

C131 Negative Numbers
1. 7
2. 3
3. 0
4. 11
5. −1
6. −1
7. 0
8. 1

C132 Negative Numbers
1. −1°C
2. −4°C
3. −3°C
4. Rise, 6°C
5. Rise, 21°C
6. Fall, 17°C

C133 Negative Numbers
Scores: –2, –1, 1, –6,
–4, –2
1 Bill and Carl
2 Ann and Fay
3 Debbie
4 8

C134 Negative Numbers
1 Wed
2 Fri
3 Tues
4 Fri
5 –9, –7, –5, –1, 1
6 17°C

C135 Percentages
$\frac{1}{2} = 0.5 = 50\% = \frac{5}{10} = \frac{50}{100}$
$\frac{1}{4} = 0.25 = 25\% = \frac{25}{100}$
$\frac{3}{4} = 0.75 = 75\% = \frac{75}{100}$
$\frac{1}{10} = 0.1 = 10\% = \frac{10}{100}$

C136 Percentages
1 ✔
2 ✔
3 ✗
4 ✔
5 ✔
6 ✗
7 ✔
8 ✔
9 ✔

C137 Percentages
1 6, 15
2 8, 40
3 4, 8
4 2.2, 4.4, 11
5 6.4, 12.8, 32
6 10, 20
7 15, 30, 45
8 31, 62, 93
9 60, 120, 180
10 9, 18, 27

C138 Percentages
1 £38.25
2 £11 580
3 £12, £1.40,
   £0.81, £180
4 68
5 80
6 144, 408

**C139 Weight and
   subtraction**
1 No
2 grams
3 21
4 23
5 1 000 g
6 29
7 4 kg
8 500 g
9 3 000 g
10 16

11 17
12 28
13 Yes
14 68 kg
15 27 kg

**C140 Place value and
   addition**
1 70
2 499
3 156
4 898
5 57 miles
6 Number plotted
   at 40
7 500
8 91
9 206
10 20
11 67, 99, 129, 209,
   301, 902
12 80
13 985
14 405
15 326

C141 Length and decimals
1 400 cm
2 3
3 Metres
4 3.0
5 5 cm *(accept
   answers in the
   range 4–6 cm)*
6 1.35 m
7 25 cm
8 No
9 0.3
10 4.5
11 50 cm
12 2.7
13 55 mm
14 4.9
15 500 m

C142 Money and shape

1

2 4
3 £1.90
4 50p, 20p, 1p
5 £3.04
6 Cylinder

7

8 Regular hexagon
9 40p
10 36p
11 square
12 sphere
13 3
14 62p
15 £1.29

**C143 Multiplication,
   division/volume**
1 18
2 6
3 2
4 60
5 1 000 ml
6 Yes
7 500 ml
8 2
9 45
10 40
11 £16
12 250 ml
13 3
14 6 r2
15 No

**C144 Number patterns/
   negative nos**
1 9
2 14
3 –6
4 8
5 –4°C
6 16
7 19
8 –6°C
9 +5
10 12
11 2°C
12 28
13 8
14 7
15 8

**C145 Decimals and
   fractions**
1 5.0
2 0.6
3 5
4 9
5 6.8
6 4
7 10
8 3
9 6.4
10 $\frac{1}{5}$
11 0.5
12 50p
13 £2.50
14 (Shade two boxes)
15 $\frac{2}{3}$

C146 Time and angles
1 South
2 North
3 Five past three
4 Quarter past ten
5 August
6 No
7 60 mins
8 21
9 31
10 4
11 Smaller

12
13 2h 15 mins
14 25 to 5 or 4:35
15 South-west

C147 Area/handling data
1 18 cm²
2 9
3 24 cm
4 5
5 25 cm²
6 *Five numbers
   with mode = 6*
7 16 cm
8 *Seven numbers
   with median = 5*
9 16 m²
10 28 cm

C148 Place value
1 106, 116
2 30 010
3 2 000
4 3 962
5 7 000
6 650
7 4 700
8 94
9 500
10 500

**C149 Decimals/fractions/
   percentages**
1 120 cm
2 0.5
3 18
4 24
5 350
6 Yes
7 £100
8 Yes
9 0.42
10 £210

C150 Time and angles
1 8:05
2 2
3 8:40
4 2h 15 mins
5 16:25
6 *(Clock reading
   17:35)*
7 11:15 am
8 8:45
9 135 seconds
10 South-west

**C151 Multiplication,
   division/volume**
1 49
2 6
3 30
4 80
5 24 cm³
6 5 cm

7 1 200 ml
8 2 400
9 80
10 320 ml

C152 Length and decimals
1 4·5, 4·9, 5, 5·4
2 400 m
3 5·7
4 70 cm
5 0·9
6 1·25 m
7 64
8 0·5
9 1·75 km
10 470

C153 Number problems
1 £23.96
2 0·52 m
3 97
4 892
5 £2005
6 £90
7 £7.31
8 10 weeks
9 £69.93
10 149

C154 Number patterns/negative nos
1 36
2 1, 3, 7, 21
3 Yes
4 –1°C
5 1°C
6 1, 2, 3, 4, 6, 8, 12, 24
7 100
8 60, 72, 84, 96
9 21
10 11

C155 Money and shape
1 2 × £1, 50p, 20p, 10p, 5p, 2 × 2p
2 £1.25
3 £25.50
4 4
5 Yes
6 Cuboid
7 £4.03
8 £11.96
9 Equilateral
10 Triangular prism

C156 Weight and subtraction
1 504
2 531
3 3500 g
4 250 g
5 9·2 kg
6 520 g
7 257
8 5·55 kg
9 6
10 255 g

C157 Mixed problems
1 8°C
2 7
3 2h 55 mins
4 95°
5 49 cm²
6 £4.20
7 No
8 3/6 or 1/2
9 32 cm
10 8

C158 Money and shape
1 75p
2 £10.35
3 3
4 9
5 £5.60
6 53p
7 8
8 Rotational
9 Rhombus
10 8

C159 Decimals/fractions/percentages
1 0·0052
2 £24
3 60
4 35
5 90
6 128
7 8
8 Yes
9 60 cm
10 11·5

C160 Time and angles
1 Acute
2 40° (Range of 30°–50°)
3 50°
4 195 mins
5 13:48
6 70°
7 110°
8 38°
9 14:10
10 130° (Range of 120°–140°)

C161 Number patterns/negative nos
1 –3, –1, 0, 5, 9
2 4°C
3 –6°C
4 13
5 6
6 10
7 2
8 –5, –2, –1, 4, 6
9 –7°C
10 5

C162 Recall Practice

+	4	2	7	3	6	5
1	5	3	8	4	7	6
4	8	6	11	7	10	9
2	6	4	9	5	8	7
5	9	7	12	8	11	10
3	7	5	10	6	9	8

+	5	3	7	4	9	6
2	7	5	9	6	11	8
8	13	11	15	12	17	14
6	11	9	13	10	15	12
10	15	13	17	14	19	16
7	12	10	14	11	16	13

C163 Recall Practice

+	8	12	9	11	13	6	10	7
10	18	22	19	21	23	16	20	17
7	15	19	16	18	20	13	17	14
12	20	24	21	23	25	18	22	19
9	17	21	18	20	22	15	19	16
11	19	23	20	22	24	17	21	18
6	14	18	15	17	19	12	16	13
8	16	20	17	19	21	14	18	15
5	13	17	14	16	18	11	15	12

+	13	24	16	18	21	17	23	25
14	27	38	30	32	35	31	37	39
19	32	43	35	37	40	36	42	44
21	34	45	37	39	42	38	44	46
18	31	42	34	36	39	35	41	43
15	28	39	31	33	36	32	38	40
17	30	41	33	35	38	34	40	42
25	38	49	41	43	46	42	48	50
16	29	40	32	34	37	33	39	41

C164 Recall Practice

–	8	11	7	9	6	10
6	2	5	1	3	0	4
3	5	8	4	6	3	7
5	3	6	2	4	1	5
2	6	9	5	7	4	8
4	4	7	3	5	2	6

–	18	20	16	19	15	17
8	10	12	8	11	7	9
13	5	7	3	6	2	4
9	9	11	7	10	6	8
12	6	8	4	7	3	5
7	11	13	9	12	8	10

C165 Recall Practice

–	20	23	19	25	18	24	22	17
10	10	13	9	15	8	14	12	7
6	14	17	13	19	12	18	16	11
7	13	16	12	18	11	17	15	10
9	11	14	10	16	9	15	13	8
12	8	11	7	13	6	12	10	5
8	12	15	11	17	10	16	14	9
13	7	10	6	12	5	11	9	4
16	4	7	3	9	2	8	6	1

–	45	37	42	36	41	39	44	35
17	28	20	25	19	24	22	27	18
19	26	18	23	17	22	20	25	16
26	19	11	16	10	15	13	18	9
15	30	22	27	21	26	24	29	20
27	18	10	15	9	14	12	17	8
18	27	19	24	18	23	21	26	17
16	29	21	26	20	25	23	28	19
29	16	8	13	7	12	10	15	6

C166 Recall Practice

×	2	5	8	1	3	6	9	10	7	4
2	4	10	16	2	6	12	18	20	14	8
5	10	25	40	5	15	30	45	50	35	20
10	20	50	80	10	30	60	90	100	70	40

×	2	5	0	4	10	3
2	4	10	0	8	20	6
10	20	50	0	40	100	30
3	6	15	0	12	30	9
5	10	25	0	20	50	15
4	8	20	0	16	40	12

C167 Recall Practice

×	2	5	10	3	9	4	6	8
2	4	10	20	6	18	8	12	16
5	10	25	50	15	45	20	30	40
10	20	50	100	30	90	40	60	80
3	6	15	30	9	27	12	18	24
9	18	45	90	27	81	36	54	72
4	8	20	40	12	36	16	24	32
6	12	30	60	18	54	24	36	48
7	14	35	70	21	63	28	42	56

×	6	4	9	8	5	11	7	12
6	36	24	54	48	30	66	42	72
4	24	16	36	32	20	44	28	48
9	54	36	81	72	45	99	63	108
8	48	32	72	64	40	88	56	96
5	30	20	45	40	25	55	35	60
11	66	44	99	88	55	121	77	132
7	42	28	63	56	35	77	49	84
12	72	48	108	96	60	132	84	144

C168 Quick Maths
Set A
1 4
2 6
3 7
4 10
5 5
6 6
7 6
8 8
9 10
10 5
11 8
12 7
13 9
14 8
15 9
16 5
17 7
18 7
19 10
20 8

Set B

#	Ans	#	Ans	#	Ans	#	Ans
1	4	5	14	11	8	15	9
2	6	6	14	12	12	16	5
3	8	7	11	13	12	17	8
4	7	8	11	14	6	18	3
5	7	9	16	15	11	19	6
6	9	10	13	16	8	20	10
7	8	11	14	17	6		
8	10	12	11	18	15		
9	8	13	13	19	6		
10	9	14	15	20	8		
11	6	15	13				
12	9	16	14				
13	10	17	13				
14	5	18	15				
15	6	19	12				
16	7	20	14				
17	10						
18	5						
19	5						
20	10						

Set D (column 4)

#	Ans
1	4
2	7
3	1
4	5
5	3
6	10
7	3
8	7
9	1
10	2
11	6
12	2
13	1
14	9
15	4
16	8
17	1
18	5
19	5
20	5

Set B (column 2)

#	Ans
1	19
2	20
3	18
4	20
5	17
6	20
7	18
8	17
9	20
10	19
11	20
12	20
13	19
14	16
15	20
16	20
17	16
18	19
19	19
20	20

Set C (column 1)

#	Ans
1	5
2	6
3	4
4	4
5	7
6	5
7	3
8	8
9	3
10	6
11	8
12	7
13	7
14	4
15	6
16	5
17	9
18	3
19	4
20	2

Set C (column 2)

#	Ans
1	8
2	5
3	5
4	8
5	5
6	6
7	6
8	7
9	3
10	7
11	7
12	6
13	4
14	9
15	8
16	7
17	8
18	6
19	9
20	9

Set D (column 1)

#	Ans
1	3
2	1
3	2
4	4
5	3
6	5
7	5
8	4
9	2
10	1
11	4
12	2
13	2
14	1
15	3
16	1
17	1
18	3
19	6
20	2

Set D (column 2)

#	Ans
1	9
2	9
3	9
4	7
5	8
6	7
7	14
8	12
9	7
10	11

C169 Quick Maths

Set A

#	Ans
1	12
2	15
3	12
4	15

C170 Quick Maths

Set A

#	Ans
1	3
2	6
3	10
4	18
5	35
6	8
7	15
8	9
9	10
10	30
11	50
12	16
13	25
14	40
15	14
16	12
17	20
18	20
19	12
20	45

Set B

#	Ans
1	16
2	25
3	12
4	6
5	40
6	10
7	12
8	45
9	20
10	20
11	70
12	40
13	16
14	30
15	15
16	90
17	8
18	80
19	35
20	18

Set C

#	Ans
1	4
2	2
3	5
4	5
5	3
6	4
7	6
8	7
9	8
10	3
11	10
12	6
13	7
14	9

C171 Quick Maths

Set A

#	Ans
1	20
2	25
3	16
4	16
5	17
6	2
7	13
8	19
9	7
10	35
11	100
12	5
13	18
14	2
15	14
16	7
17	10
18	16
19	12
20	9

Set B

#	Ans
1	9
2	14
3	13
4	12
5	30
6	12
7	15
8	15
9	15
10	3
11	8
12	6
13	17
14	3
15	14
16	13
17	4
18	40

	19	15
	20	7
Set C	1	4
	2	13
	3	11
	4	45
	5	11
	6	16
	7	6
	8	9
	9	10
	10	13
	11	4
	12	9
	13	15
	14	6
	15	3
	16	40
	17	19
	18	8
	19	6
	20	18
Set D	1	8
	2	14
	3	50
	4	8
	5	4
	6	16
	7	50
	8	5
	9	14
	10	7
	11	60
	12	14
	13	20
	14	5
	15	7
	16	14
	17	12
	18	10
	19	19
	20	10

C172 Quick Maths

Set A	1	20
	2	17
	3	19
	4	19
	5	18
	6	20
	7	16
	8	20
	9	17
	10	19
	11	16
	12	20
	13	20
	14	18
	15	20
	16	19
	17	20
	18	20
	19	20
	20	19
Set B	1	24
	2	23

	3	24
	4	25
	5	24
	6	24
	7	23
	8	21
	9	24
	10	25
	11	22
	12	24
	13	25
	14	22
	15	21
	16	23
	17	23
	18	25
	19	22
	20	22
Set C	1	11
	2	10
	3	13
	4	6
	5	10
	6	8
	7	7
	8	7
	9	12
	10	9
	11	8
	12	13
	13	9
	14	8
	15	10
	16	12
	17	8
	18	9
	19	11
	20	14
Set D	1	14
	2	17
	3	16
	4	17
	5	13
	6	16
	7	18
	8	9
	9	14
	10	11
	11	13
	12	9
	13	15
	14	16
	15	10
	16	8
	17	15
	18	12
	19	18
	20	17

C173 Quick Maths

Set A	1	42
	2	48
	3	44
	4	50
	5	45
	6	43

	7	42
	8	44
	9	45
	10	47
	11	43
	12	46
	13	40
	14	46
	15	50
	16	43
	17	41
	18	45
	19	47
	20	44
Set B	1	85
	2	100
	3	82
	4	91
	5	92
	6	75
	7	91
	8	82
	9	95
	10	73
	11	75
	12	80
	13	76
	14	73
	15	93
	16	74
	17	71
	18	62
	19	99
	20	92
Set C	1	25
	2	18
	3	19
	4	27
	5	18
	6	29
	7	18
	8	19
	9	16
	10	30
	11	19
	12	29
	13	23
	14	31
	15	17
	16	13
	17	21
	18	17
	19	19
	20	25
Set D	1	51
	2	35
	3	42
	4	35
	5	45
	6	55
	7	68
	8	49
	9	39
	10	29
	11	57
	12	46

	13	27
	14	37
	15	33
	16	66
	17	48
	18	48
	19	29
	20	45

C174 Quick Maths

Set A	1	24
	2	48
	3	24
	4	28
	5	18
	6	32
	7	28
	8	54
	9	36
	10	42
	11	63
	12	42
	13	56
	14	36
	15	64
	16	21
	17	32
	18	24
	19	49
	20	48
Set B	1	56
	2	27
	3	42
	4	63
	5	64
	6	36
	7	49
	8	48
	9	35
	10	81
	11	28
	12	72
	13	24
	14	56
	15	54
	16	24
	17	32
	18	45
	19	36
	20	72
Set C	1	8
	2	9
	3	5
	4	9
	5	9
	6	9
	7	7
	8	7
	9	6
	10	7
	11	5
	12	8
	13	8
	14	10
	15	6
	16	6

155

	17	8
	18	7
	19	5
	20	6
Set D	1	3
	2	8
	3	9
	4	6
	5	5
	6	9
	7	7
	8	7
	9	7
	10	4
	11	9
	12	8
	13	6
	14	3
	15	8
	16	4
	17	6
	18	7
	19	8
	20	6

C175 Quick Maths

Set A	1	27
	2	42
	3	36
	4	9
	5	33
	6	44
	7	21
	8	8
	9	84
	10	45
	11	5
	12	29
	13	73
	14	16
	15	19
	16	6
	17	43
	18	25
	19	46
	20	6
Set B	1	8
	2	34
	3	6
	4	32
	5	46
	6	7
	7	16
	8	6
	9	85
	10	60
	11	57
	12	45
	13	40
	14	5
	15	24
	16	7
	17	36
	18	43
	19	25
	20	28

Set C	1	9
	2	9
	3	41
	4	24
	5	19
	6	4
	7	47
	8	42
	9	18
	10	95
	11	8
	12	87
	13	24
	14	44
	15	8
	16	51
	17	100
	18	16
	19	64
	20	55
Set D	1	9
	2	28
	3	54
	4	9
	5	36
	6	15
	7	5
	8	56
	9	8
	10	59
	11	6
	12	71
	13	25
	14	49
	15	56
	16	90
	17	25
	18	7
	19	74
	20	38

C177 KS2 Practice Tests

1	17
2	195
3	300
4	40
5	31
6	Pentagon
7	30 mm
8	8
9	73
10	964
11	$\frac{3}{5}$
12	East
13	45
14	£45
15	62p
16	500 ml
17	Smaller
18	2
19	4000g
20	(kite shape)
21	11, 15, 23
22	£2.75

23	−2°C
24	7
25	75

C179 KS2 Practice Tests

1	8
2	201
3	70
4	9
5	24
6	14
7	90
8	Hexagon
9	25
10	2
11	East
12	8
13	97
14	4
15	500 g
16	(trapezium shape)
17	Cylinder
18	£35
19	38p
20	3000 ml
21	8, 12, 26
22	14
23	11:00 am
24	45
25	£4.64

C181 KS2 Practice Tests

1	750
2	2500
3	7
4	0·5
5	2010
6	6500 g
7	54
8	8:45
9	25 cm²
10	13:10 or 1:10
11	3
12	3°C
13	560
14	£50
15	2·7–2·8
16	Parallelogram
17	157
18	80
19	12 cm²
20	£8.40
21	9, 24, 45
22	30
23	740 or 700
24	10
25	Square based pyramid

C183 KS2 Practice Tests

1	32
2	4000
3	63
4	105 mm

5	40004
6	36
7	8
8	90°
9	36 cm
10	3:35
11	120° (accept 110°–130°)
12	6
13	Yes
14	90
15	400 g
16	403
17	0·329
18	36
19	10
20	195 mins
21	8, 1, 6
22	800 m
23	£25.80
24	19 cm
25	36

C185 KS2 Practice Tests

1	9
2	246
3	12
4	$\frac{1}{4}$
5	180°
6	4·08 km
7	240
8	14:00
9	12 cm
10	14:10
11	15
12	8°C
13	0·4
14	£24
15	(Arrow to show 0·5)
16	2
17	208
18	20
19	240
20	30° (accept 20°–40°)
21	81, 64, 9
22	7
23	1006
24	13
25	9